# TEACHING

## HARCOURT SCIENCE

# RESOURCES

**Harcourt School Publishers**

Orlando • Boston • Dallas • Chicago • San Diego

www.harcourtschool.com

Printed in the United States of America

ISBN 0-15-314754-7

1 2 3 4 5 6 7 8 9 10 054 2002 2001 2000 99

HARCOURT SCIENCE

# Contents

## Maps, Charts, Patterns, Graphs TR110–123

# School-Home Connection

Harcourt Science

## Chapter Content

Today we begin a new chapter in science. Your child will be learning about living and non-living things. We will be doing science activities that use the senses to help learn about the things around us. We will also observe and learn about the characteristics of living and nonliving things.

## Science Process Skills

Learning to **observe** carefully is one of the most important skills of science. Observing is more than looking with the eyes. The senses of smell, hearing, touch, and sometimes taste also play a part in making careful observations.

To encourage the ability to observe carefully and accurately, together walk around your home and choose one thing for your child to observe closely in each room. Encourage your child to use as many senses as possible to describe the things he or she observes.

## Science Fun

Children's books can provide fun science connections, as they often have science ideas woven into their stories. Pointing these connections out helps children see that science is part of life both inside and outside the classroom.

***Animals and Their World*** by Sally Morgan (Young Discoverers: Biology Facts and Experiments Series, 1996).

Your child may enjoy learning about how animals use their senses in *Animals and Their World* by Sally Morgan. This book contains many activities in addition to providing information about how animals use their senses to hunt for food, protect themselves, and communicate with one another.

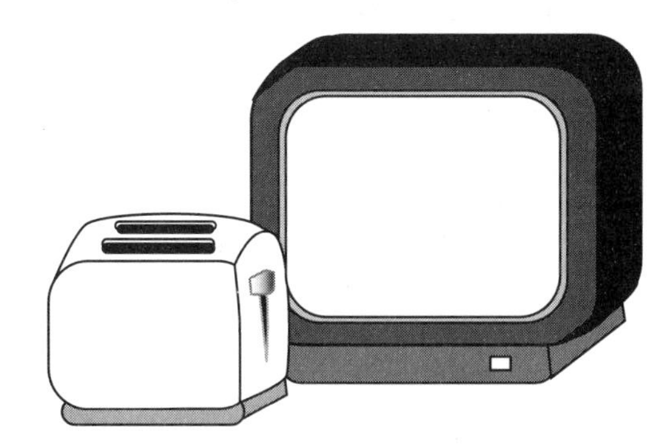

## Activity Materials from Home

Dear Family Member:

To do the activities in this chapter, we will need some materials that you may have around the house. Look at the items listed at the right. If possible, please send these things to school with your child.

Your help and support are appreciated!

- ____ **piece of fruit**
- ____ **small rocks**

# La escuela y la casa

Harcourt Ciencias

## Contenido del capítulo

Hoy comenzamos un nuevo capítulo de ciencias. Su hijo(a) aprenderá sobre los seres vivos y no vivos. Realizaremos actividades científicas usando los sentidos para aprender sobre las cosas que nos rodean. También observaremos y aprenderemos las características de los seres vivos y no vivos.

## Destrezas del proceso científico

Aprender a **observar** detalladamente es una de las destrezas más importantes de las ciencias. Observar es más que mirar con los ojos. Los sentidos del olfato, la audición, el tacto y algunas veces del gusto también contribuyen a hacer observaciones detalladas.

Para estimular la habilidad de observar detalladamente y con precisión, camine con su hijo(a) por su casa y elija algo para que él (ella) lo observe en detalle en cada habitación. Anímelo(a) a que use tantos sentidos como sea posible al describir las cosas que observa.

## Diversión

Los libros infantiles pueden proporcionar conexiones de ciencias divertidas, ya que a menudo sus historias contienen ideas científicas. Señalar estas conexiones ayuda a los niños a comprender que las ciencias forman parte de la vida dentro y fuera del salón de clases.

***Animals and Their World*** de Sally Morgan (Young Discoverers: Biology Facts and Experiments Series, 1996).

Quizás su hijo(a) se divierta aprendiendo cómo los animales usan sus sentidos en *Animals and Their World* de Sally Morgan. Este libro contiene muchas actividades además de proporcionar información de cómo los animales usan sus sentidos para cazar, protegerse y comunicarse con los demás.

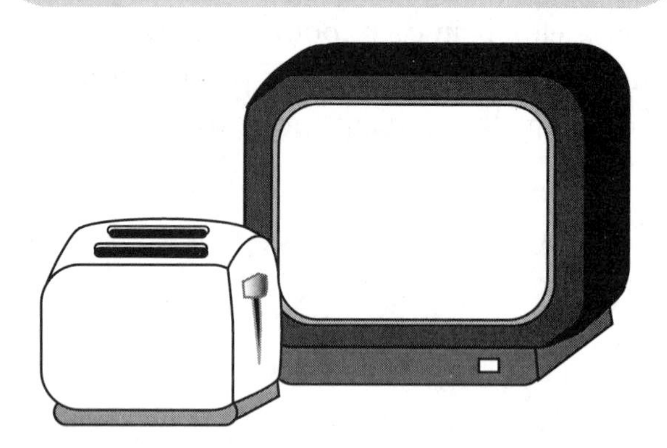

## Materiales de casa para la actividad

Querido familiar:

Para hacer las actividades de este capítulo, necesitaremos algunos materiales que tal vez tenga en la casa. Observe los artículos de la lista de la derecha. Si es posible, por favor envíe estas cosas con su hijo(a) a la escuela.

¡Gracias por su ayuda y su apoyo!

____ **fruta**

____ **rocas pequeñas**

# School-Home Connection

Harcourt Science

## Chapter Content

Today in science we began a chapter on plants. We will be doing science activities that identify the parts of a plant, how a plant grows, and what a plant needs to live and grow.

## Science Process Skills

Learning to **observe** carefully is one of the most important skills in science. By observing carefully and keeping careful records of what was observed, scientists can remember what they have done during an experiment and draw conclusions about what they have observed.

Help your child observe and record the changes that the seed in **Science Fun** undergoes as it grows into a mature plant. Encourage your child to draw the seed and resulting plant every few days. Help him or her record how much water is given, measure the height of the plant, and so on.

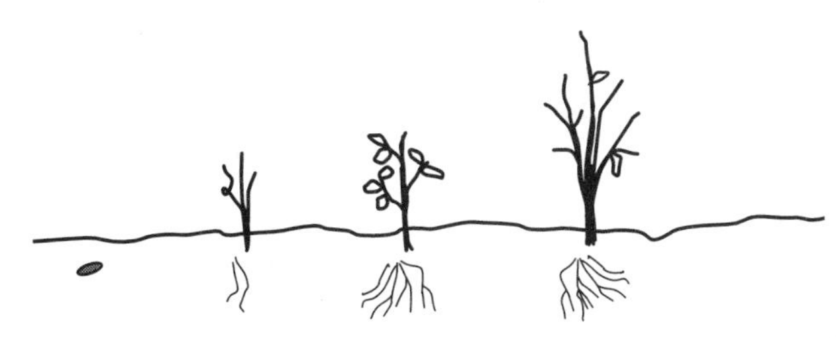

## Science Fun

With your child, select and grow an indoor or outdoor plant from seed. You might choose an ornamental plant, such as a coleus, or a garden plant, such as parsley or beans.

**What You Need**

- seeds
- water
- potting soil
- container such as a paper cup

**What to Do**

1. Fill the cup three-fourths full of soil. Be sure the soil is damp, but not wet.
2. Plant the seeds by following package directions.
3. Place the cup in a sunny window or in a well-lighted area.
4. Keep a record of all the things you and your child do to care for the plant. Be sure not to over-water your plant.

## Activity Materials from Home

Dear Family Member:

To do the activities in this chapter, we will need some materials that you may have around the house. Look at the items listed at the right. If possible, please send these things to school with your child.

Your help and support are appreciated!

____ **carrot with leafy top**
____ **unsharpened pencil**

# La escuela y la casa

Harcourt Ciencias

## Contenido del capítulo

Hoy comenzamos un nuevo capítulo de ciencias. Su hijo(a) aprenderá sobre las plantas. Realizaremos actividades científicas que identifican las partes de una planta, cómo crece una planta y qué necesita una planta para vivir y crecer.

## Destrezas del proceso científico

Aprender a **observar** detalladamente es una de las destrezas más importantes de las ciencias. Al observar detalladamente y anotar con cuidado lo que se ha observado, los científicos pueden recordar lo que han hecho durante un experimento y sacar conclusiones sobre de lo que han observado.

Ayude a su hijo(a) a observar y anotar los cambios que sufre la semilla en **Diversión** a medida que crece y se convierte en una planta madura. Anime a su hijo(a) a dibujar la semilla y la planta a medida que crece cada dos o tres días. Ayúdelo a anotar cuánta agua se le da, medir la altura de la planta y así sucesivamente.

## Diversión

Con su hijo(a), seleccione y cultive una semilla de una planta de interior o exterior. Quizás elija una planta ornamental como un coleo o una planta de jardín como perejil o frijoles.

**Lo que necesitas**

- semillas
- agua
- tierra para plantar
- recipiente como un vaso de papel

**Lo que vas a hacer**

1. Llena el vaso con tres cuartos de tierra. Asegúrate de que la tierra esté húmeda, pero no empapada.
2. Siembra las semillas siguiendo las instrucciones del paquete.
3. Coloca el vaso en una ventana donde le dé el sol o en un área bien iluminada.
4. Anote todas las cosas que Ud. y su hijo(a) hacen para cuidar la planta. Asegúrese de que no le echen mucha agua a la planta.

## Materiales de casa para la actividad

Querido familiar:

Para hacer las actividades en este capítulo, necesitaremos algunos materiales que tal vez tenga en la casa. Observe los artículos de la lista de la derecha. Si es posible, por favor envíe estas cosas con su hijo(a) a la escuela.

¡Gracias por su ayuda y su apoyo!

____ **zanahoria con el tope frondoso**
____ **lápiz sin punta**

# School-Home Connection

Harcourt Science

## Chapter Content

Today we begin a new chapter in science. Your child will be learning about different kinds of animals, what their needs are, and how some kinds of animals grow. We will be doing science activities such as observing animals and making model animals.

## Science Process Skills

Just as students learn to sequence events in math, they learn to **sequence** the steps of a process in science. The life stages of plants and animals lend themselves to the reinforcement of this skill.

With your child, select an animal to study. Learn about the animal's life cycle, where it lives, and what things it needs to survive. Help your child draw pictures of the animal at different stages of its life. Mix up the pictures, and let your child sequence them from young animal to adult. Encourage your child to tell you how the animal has changed in each picture.

## Science Fun

Children's books can provide fun science connections, as they often have science ideas woven into their stories. Pointing out these connections helps children see that science is part of life both inside and outside the classroom.

*Animal Homes* by Colin Threadgall (Crown Publishers Inc., 1996).

Your child may enjoy reading and observing different kinds of animal homes in Colin Threadgall's *Animal Homes*. Some of the animals featured in this book are the kingfisher, mole, polar bear, and platypus. Encourage your child to pick an animal's favorite home, and draw a picture of that home.

## Activity Materials from Home

Dear Family Member:

To do the activities in this chapter, we will need some materials that you may have around the house. Look at the items listed at the right. If possible, please send these things to school with your child.

Your help and support are appreciated!

- ____ **leaves on a twig**
- ____ **small rocks and twigs**
- ____ **bottle cap**
- ____ **toothpicks**
- ____ **wax paper**

# La escuela y la casa

Harcourt Ciencias

## Contenido del capítulo

Hoy comenzamos un nuevo capítulo de ciencias. Su hijo(a) aprenderá sobre los diferentes tipos de animales, cuáles son sus necesidades y cómo crecen ciertos tipos de animales. Realizaremos actividades científicas como observar los animales y hacer modelos de animales.

## Destrezas del proceso científico

Así como los estudiantes aprenden a ordenar los sucesos en matemáticas, también aprenden la **secuencia** de los pasos en un proceso científico. Las etapas de la vida de las plantas y los animales les permiten reforzar esta destreza.

Con su hijo(a), seleccione un animal para estudiarlo. Aprenda sobre los ciclos de vida del animal, dónde vive y cuáles son las cosas que necesita para sobrevivir. Ayude a su hijo(a) a hacer dibujos de un animal en las diferentes etapas de su vida. Mezcle las ilustraciones y deje que su hijo(a) las coloque en **secuencia** desde un animal joven hasta un adulto. Anímelo(a) a decir cómo ha cambiado el animal en cada dibujo.

## Diversión

Los libros infantiles pueden proporcionar conexiones de ciencias divertidas, ya que a menudo sus historias contienen ideas científicas. Señalar estas conexiones ayuda a los niños a comprender que las ciencias forman parte de la vida dentro y fuera del salón de clases.

*Animal Homes* de Colin Threadgall (Crown Publishers Inc., 1996).

Quizás su hijo(a) se divierta leyendo y observando los diferentes tipos de hogares de los animales en *Animal Homes* de Colin Threadgall. Algunos de los animales presentados en este libro son martín pescador, topo, oso polar y ornitorrinco. Anime a su hijo(a) a elegir el hogar de un animal favorito y a hacer un dibujo de ese hogar.

## Materiales de casa para la actividad

Querido familiar:

Para hacer las actividades en este capítulo, necesitaremos algunos materiales que tal vez tenga en la casa. Observe los artículos de la lista de la derecha. Si es posible, por favor envíe estas cosas con su hijo(a) a la escuela.

¡Gracias por su ayuda y su apoyo!

- ____ **hojas en una ramita**
- ____ **rocas pequeñas y ramitas**
- ____ **tapa de una botella**
- ____ **palillos de dientes**
- ____ **papel encerado**

# School-Home Connection

Harcourt Science

## Chapter Content

Today we begin a new chapter in science. Your child will be learning about how animals use plants to meet their needs as well as how animals can help plants. We will also study how people use both plants and animals to meet their needs. We will be doing science activities that study different ways animals use plants, how animals help plants, and different ways people use plants and animals.

## Science Process Skills

Learning to **classify** objects or events into categories is an important skill in science. By placing things into similar groups, scientists can make generalizations about how the world works or how things are related to one another.

With your child walk around your home. After observing a number of objects, decide on two groups into which you could sort the items. For example, you might sort items into those made of plastic and those not made of plastic, or those that use electricity and those that don't. As your child studies the information in this chapter, he or she will learn that this sorting process is one step in classifying things.

## Science Fun

Children's books can provide fun science connections, as they often have science ideas woven into their stories. Pointing these connections out helps children see that science is part of life both inside and outside the classroom.

*Warm as Wool* by Scott Russell Sanders (Simon & Schuster, 1998).

Your child may enjoy reading *Warm as Wool* by Scott Russell Sanders. The story is set in 1804 as a family moves across country. Once in their new home, Betsy Ward, the mother, buys a flock of sheep. She then spins cloth and makes clothes from the wool in order to keep her family warm during the winter.

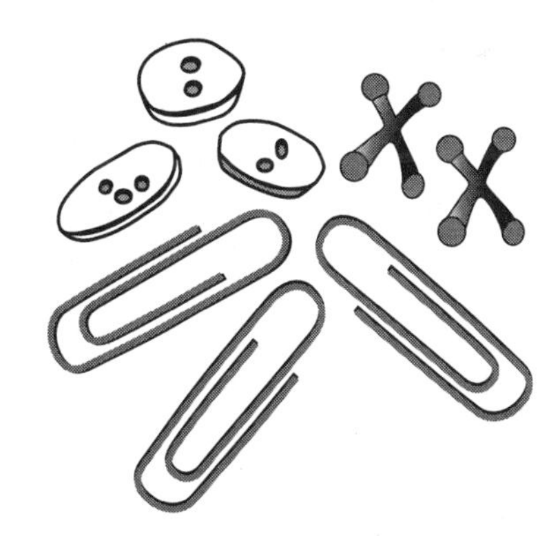

## Activity Materials from Home

Dear Family Member:

To do the activities in this chapter, we will need some materials that you may have around the house. Look at the items listed at the right. If possible, please send these things to school with your child.

Your help and support are appreciated!

____ **string or yarn**
____ **Velcro**
____ **cotton balls**
____ **sandpaper**
____ **Styrofoam balls**

# La escuela y la casa

**Harcourt Ciencias**

## Contenido del capítulo

Hoy comenzamos un nuevo capítulo de ciencias. Su hijo(a) aprenderá sobre cómo las personas, los animales y las plantas se necesitan unas a otras. Realizaremos actividades científicas que estudian las diferentes formas en que los animales usan las plantas, cómo los animales ayudan a las plantas y las diferentes formas en que las personas usan las plantas y los animales.

## Destrezas del proceso científico

Aprender a **clasificar** objetos o sucesos en categorías es una destreza importante de las ciencias. Al colocar cosas en grupos iguales, los científicos pueden hacer generalizaciones sobre cómo trabaja el mundo o cómo se relacionan las cosas entre sí.

Camine con su hijo(a) por su casa. Después de observar un número de objetos, decida en dos grupos en los cuales podría ordenar los artículos. Por ejemplo, quizás quiera ordenar lo artículos en los que son de plástico y los que no son de plástico o los que usan electricidad y los que no. Mientras su hijo(a) estudia la información en este capítulo, él aprenderá que este proceso de clasificación es un paso para ordenar las cosas.

## Diversión

Los libros infantiles pueden proporcionar conexiones de ciencias divertidas, ya que a menudo sus historias contienen ideas científicas. Señalar estas conexiones ayuda a los niños a comprender que las ciencias forman parte de la vida dentro y fuera del salón de clases.

*Warm as Wool* de Scott Russell Sanders (Simon & Schuster, 1998).

Quizás su hijo(a) se divierta leyendo *Warm as Wool* de Scott Russell Sanders. La historia ocurre en 1804 a medida que una familia se movilizaba por el país. Una vez que estaban en su nuevo hogar, Betsy Ward, la madre, compra un rebaño de ovejas. Después hila y hace ropa de la lana para poder mantener a su familia abrigada durante el invierno.

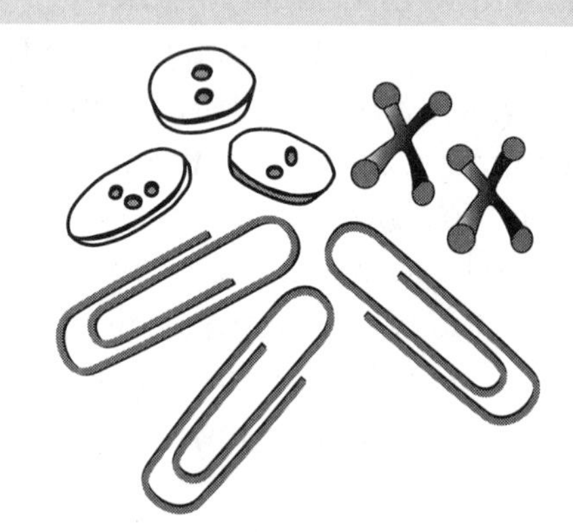

## Materiales de casa para la actividad

Querido familiar:

Para hacer las actividades en este capítulo, necesitaremos algunos materiales que tal vez tenga en la casa. Observe los artículos de la lista de la derecha. Si es posible, por favor envíe estas cosas con su hijo(a) a la escuela.

¡Gracias por su ayuda y su apoyo!

- ____ **hilo o estambre**
- ____ **Velcro**
- ____ **bolitas de algodón**
- ____ **papel de lija**
- ____ **bolitas de estireno**

# School-Home Connection

Harcourt Science

## Chapter Content

Today in science we began studying about where plants and animals live. Your child will be learning about living things in a forest, desert, rain forest, and ocean. We will be doing science activities that help us study the different kinds of plants and animals that live in these places.

## Science Process Skills

Learning to **draw conclusions** is an important skill of science. Students not only need to draw conclusions from the activities they do, but also from the materials they read.

Go to the library together and read *The Great Kapok Tree: A Tale of the Amazon Rain Forest* (Harcourt Brace, 1998). In this story, a man is set to cut down a great kapok tree that is home to a variety of animals. These animals try to persuade the man not to destroy their home. Help your child draw a conclusion as to what would happen to the animals in the forest if the tree were to be cut down.

## Science Fun

Make a mini-terrarium out of a two-liter soft drink bottle.

### What You Need

- scissors
- potting soil
- spoon
- several small plants
- clean 2-L bottle
- clean gravel
- water
- plastic wrap
- rubber band

### What to Do

1. Carefully cut off the top of the 2-L bottle.
2. Help your child make a thin layer of gravel, followed by a thicker layer of soil, in the bottom of the bottle.
3. Use the spoon to gently place the plants in the soil. Press the plants firmly in place.
4. Water the plants well.
5. Cover the top of the bottle with plastic wrap and secure with a rubber band.
6. Observe the terrarium for several weeks and record what you observe.

## Activity Materials from Home

Dear Family Member:

To do the activities in this chapter, we will need some materials that you may have around the house. Look at the items listed at the right. If possible, please send these things to school with your child.

Your help and support are appreciated!

____ **plastic bag, sandwich size**
____ **paper towels**
____ **wax paper**
____ **alfalfa seeds**
____ **cotton balls**
____ **plastic film canisters**

# La escuela y la casa

**Harcourt Ciencias**

## Contenido del capítulo

Hoy comenzamos un nuevo capítulo de ciencias. Su hijo(a) aprenderá sobre los seres vivos del bosque, del desierto, del bosque tropical y del océano. Realizaremos actividades científicas que nos ayudarán a estudiar los diferentes tipos de plantas y animales que viven en estos lugares.

## Destrezas del proceso científico

Aprender a **sacar conclusiones** es una destreza importante de las ciencias. Los estudiantes no sólo necesitan sacar conclusiones de las actividades que hacen sino también de los materiales que leen.

Vayan a la biblioteca y lean *The Great Kapok Tree: A Tale of the Amazon Rain Forest* (Harcourt Brace, 1998). En esta historia un hombre quiere cortar un miraguano que es el hogar de una serie de animales. Estos animales tratan de persuadir al hombre a no destruir su hogar. Ayude a su hijo(a) a sacar una conclusión de lo que les pasaría a los animales del bosque si se talara el árbol.

## Diversión

Hacer un terrario en miniatura de una botella de refresco.

**Lo que necesitas**

- tijeras
- tierra para plantar
- cuchara
- algunas plantas pequeñas
- botella limpia de 2L
- gravilla limpia
- agua
- papel de plástico
- elástico

**Lo que vas a hacer**

1. Corta con cuidado el borde superior de la botella de 2L.
2. Ayude a su hijo(a) a hacer una capa de gravilla delgada, seguida de una capa más gruesa de tierra en el fondo de la botella.
3. Usa la cuchara para colocar suavemente las plantas en la tierra. Presiona las plantas con firmeza en el lugar.
4. Riega bien las plantas.
5. Cubre la parte superior de la botella con papel de plástico y asegúrela con un elástico.
6. Observa el terrario por algunas semanas y anota lo que observas.

## Materiales de casa para la actividad

Querido familiar:

Para hacer las actividades en este capítulo, necesitaremos algunos materiales que tal vez tenga en la casa. Observe los artículos de la lista de la derecha. Si es posible, por favor envíe estas cosas con su hijo(a) a la escuela.

¡Gracias por su ayuda y su apoyo!

____ **bolsa de plástico del tamaño de un sándwich**
____ **toallas de papel**
____ **papel encerado**
____ **semillas de alfalfa**
____ **bolitas de algodón**
____ **recipientes de plástico de rollos de películas**

# School-Home Connection

Harcourt Science

## Chapter Content

Today we begin a new chapter in science. Your child will be learning about the Earth's land. We will be doing science activities that include observing rocks and comparing different kinds of soil.

## Science Process Skills

Learning to **classify** is an important skill of science. Children are asked to classify based upon an observable property. Children also use observation to aid in classifying things.

Encourage your child to observe and classify. Together with your child select rocks or small stones to study. Use observation to identify traits that you can use to place the objects into different groups. Encourage your child to find several ways to classify the same group of objects.

## Science Fun

Children's books can provide fun science connections, as they often have science ideas woven into their stories. Pointing these connections out helps children see that science is part of life both inside and outside the classroom.

*From Sand to Glass* by Ali Mitgutsch, Marlene Reidel, and Annegert Fuchshuber (Charolrhoda Books, Inc., 1983).

Your child may enjoy learning about how sand can be melted to make glass in *From Sand to Glass.* This book describes glass-making and how molten glass is blown into things such as bottles and windowpanes.

## Activity Materials from Home

Dear Family Member:

To do the activities in this chapter, we will need some materials that you may have around the house. Please note the items at the right. If possible, please send these things to school with your child.

Your help and support are appreciated!

- ___ **small rocks**
- ___ **paper plates**
- ___ **plastic spoons**
- ___ **plastic zip-top sandwich bags**

# La escuela y la casa

Harcourt Ciencias

## Contenido del capítulo

Hoy comenzamos un nuevo capítulo de ciencias. Su hijo(a) aprenderá sobre la superficie de la Tierra. Realizaremos actividades científicas que incluyen observar rocas y comparar diferentes tipos de suelo.

## Destrezas del proceso científico

Aprender a **clasificar** es una destreza importante de las ciencias. A los niños se les pidió que clasificaran basados en una propiedad que se pudiera observar. También usan la observación para clasificar las cosas.

Anime a su hijo(a) a observar y clasificar. Juntos, seleccionen rocas o piedras pequeñas para estudiarlas. Usen la observación para identificar características que pueden usar para colocar los objetos en diferentes grupos. Anímelo a hallar algunas formas de clasificar el mismo grupo de objetos.

## Diversión

Los libros infantiles pueden proporcionar conexiones de ciencias divertidas, ya que a menudo sus historias contienen ideas científicas. Señalar estas conexiones ayuda a los niños a comprender que las ciencias forman parte de la vida dentro y fuera del salón de clases.

***From Sand to Glass*** de Ali Mitgutsch, Marlene Reidel y Annegert Fuchshuber (Charolrhoda Books, Inc., 1983).

Quizás su hijo(a) se divierta aprendiendo sobre cómo la arena se puede fundir para hacer vidrio en *From Sand to Glass*. Este libro describe la elaboración de vidrio y cómo el vidrio fundido se moldea en cosas como botellas y ventanas de cristal.

## Materiales de casa para la actividad

Querido familiar:

Para hacer las actividades en este capítulo, necesitaremos algunos materiales que tal vez tenga en la casa. Observe los artículos de la lista de la derecha. Si es posible, por favor envíe estas cosas con su hijo(a) a la escuela.

¡Gracias por su ayuda y su apoyo!

____ **rocas pequeñas**
____ **platos de papel**
____ **cucharas de plástico**
____ **bolsas de plástico con cierre para sándwich**

# School-Home Connection

Harcourt Science

## Chapter Content

Today we begin a new chapter in science. Your child will be learning about Earth's air and water. We will be doing science activities that investigate the air around us. We will also learn about where fresh water and salt water are found on Earth.

## Science Process Skills

Learning to **communicate** is an important skill in science. By communicating through words or drawings, children can convey the results of a science activity.

Use the picture you and your child draw as the conclusion to **Science Fun** as a writing prompt. Have your child think of two or three words that describe a waterless day. Children might suggest words such as dry, thirsty, or dusty. Help your child write sentences for each word he or she lists.

## Science Fun

Everyone uses water every day. This activity will help your child understand how much we depend on this important resource.

Talk with your child about how your family uses water. Make a list of all the things you can think of. The list might include bathing, cooking, drinking, cleaning, brushing teeth, flushing toilets, and so on. Encourage your child to think of less obvious ways water is used, such as to grow the plants and animals we use for food.

When the list is complete, have your child think about a day without water. Work together to draw a picture of what this day would be like.

## Activity Materials from Home

Dear Family Member:

To do the activities in this chapter, we will need some materials that you may have around the house. Please note the items listed at the right. If possible, please send these things to school with your child.

Your help and support are appreciated!

- ____ **plastic produce bag**
- ____ **plastic spoons**
- ____ **plastic wrap**
- ____ **small marbles**
- ____ **salt**
- ____ **aluminum foil**

# La escuela y la casa

**Harcourt Ciencias**

## Contenido del capítulo

Hoy comenzamos un nuevo capítulo de ciencias. Su hijo(a) aprenderá sobre el aire y el agua de la Tierra. Realizaremos actividades científicas que investigan el aire que nos rodea. También aprenderemos dónde se hallan el agua dulce y el agua salada en la Tierra.

## Destrezas del proceso científico

Aprender a **comunicar** es una destreza importante de las ciencias. Al comunicarse a través de las palabras o ilustraciones, los niños pueden expresar los resultados de una actividad científica.

Usen el dibujo que Ud. y su hijo(a) hicieron en la conclusión de **Diversión** como una sugerencia para hacer la descripción por escrito. Pida a su hijo(a) que piense en dos o tres palabras que describan un día sin agua. Los niños podrían sugerir palabras como seco, sediento o polvoriento. Ayude a su hijo(a) a escribir oraciones para cada palabra que enumere.

## Diversión

Todo el mundo usa el agua todos los días. Esta actividad ayudará a su hijo(a) a comprender cuánto dependemos de este importante recurso.

Hable con su hijo(a) sobre cómo su familia usa el agua. Elabore una lista de todas las cosas en las que puede pensar. La lista debe incluir bañarse, cocinar, beber, limpiar, cepillarse los dientes, bajar la palanca del baño y así sucesivamente. Anime a su hijo(a) para que piense en las maneras menos obvias en que se usa el agua como cultivar las plantas y criar los animales que usamos como alimento.

Cuando la lista esté completa, pida a su hijo(a) que piense sobre un día sin agua. Trabajen para elaborar un dibujo de cómo sería ese día.

## Materiales de casa para la actividad

Querido familiar:

Para hacer las actividades de este capítulo, necesitaremos algunos materiales que tal vez tenga en la casa. Observe los artículos de la lista de la derecha. Si es posible, por favor envíe estas cosas con su hijo(a) a la escuela.

¡Gracias por su ayuda y su apoyo!

- ____ **bolsa de plástico**
- ____ **cucharas de plástico**
- ____ **papel de plástico**
- ____ **canicas pequeñas**
- ____ **sal**
- ____ **papel de aluminio**

# School-Home Connection

Harcourt Science

## Chapter Content

Today we begin a new chapter in science. Your child will be learning about the weather. We will be doing activities that investigate sky conditions, measure temperature, observe wind direction, and find out how clouds are formed.

## Science Process Skills

Learning to **compare** is an important skill of science. Children are asked to identify common and distinguishing characteristics among objects or events.

To encourage the ability to compare, help your child observe the weather for one week. Record your observations at the end of each day. Compare how each day's weather is similar to or different from the last. Encourage your child to use comparison words such as warmer, cooler, windier, wetter, and so on.

## Science Fun

Make a decorative wind sock to hang outdoors. Your child can use the sock to observe the wind.

**You Will Need**

- large sheet of tissue paper or light cloth
- long, thin strips of tissue paper
- several chenille sticks
- tape
- string or yarn
- scissors

**What to Do**

1. Roll the large sheet of tissue paper into a tube that has a 4-in. diameter. Secure with tape.
2. Use chenille sticks to form two rings that are the same size as the diameter of the tube. Attach one ring to one end of the tube with tape.
3. Attach the tissue strips around one end of the tube so they hang freely.
4. Cut three 3-in. pieces of string. Tape the pieces equidistant around the top of the tube. Tie the free ends of the strings together. Add a longer piece of string for hanging. Hang.

## Activity Materials from Home

Dear Family Member:

To do the activities in this chapter, we will need some materials that you may have around the house. Please note the items at the right. If possible, please send these things to school with your child.

Your help and support are appreciated!

____ **drinking straws**
____ **toothpicks**

# La escuela y la casa

**Harcourt Ciencias**

## Contenido del capítulo

Hoy comenzamos un nuevo capítulo de ciencias. Su hijo(a) aprenderá sobre el clima. Realizaremos actividades científicas que investigan las condiciones del cielo, medir la temperatura, observar la dirección del viento y descubrir cómo se forman las nubes.

## Destrezas del proceso científico

Aprender a **comparar** es una destreza importante de ciencias. A los niños se les pide que identifiquen características comunes y distintivas entre objetos o sucesos.

Para estimular la habilidad de comparar, ayude a su hijo(a) a observar el clima por una semana. Anote sus observaciones al final de cada día. Compare cómo el clima de cada día se parece o se diferencia al del día anterior. Anime a su hijo(a) para que use palabras de comparación como más caliente, más frío, más húmedo y otras.

## Diversión

Hacer una manga de aire para colgarla afuera. Su hijo(a) puede usar la manga para observar el viento.

**Lo que necesitas**

- hoja grande de papel de seda o tela suave
- tiras largas y delgadas de papel de seda
- algunas palitos de felpilla
- cinta adhesiva
- hilo o estambre
- tijeras

**Lo que vas a hacer**

1. Enrolla la hoja grande de papel de seda en un tubo que tenga un diámetro de 4 pulg. Asegúralo con la cinta adhesiva.
2. Usa las pajitas de felpilla para formar dos anillos que sean del mismo tamaño del diámetro del tubo. Amarra un anillo a uno de los extremos del tubo con cinta adhesiva.
3. Amarra las tiras de papel de seda alrededor de uno de los extremos del tubo de manera que cuelguen libremente.
4. Corta tres pedazos de hilo de 3 pulg. Pega los pedazos a igual distancia alrededor de la punta del tubo. Amarra juntos los extremos libres de los hilos. Agrega un pedazo más largo de hilo para que cuelgue. Cuelga la manga.

## Materiales de casa para la actividad

Querido familiar:

Para hacer las actividades de este capítulo, necesitaremos algunos materiales que tal vez tenga en la casa. Observe los artículos de la lista de la derecha. Si es posible, por favor envíe estas cosas con su hijo(a) a la escuela.

¡Gracias por su ayuda y su apoyo!

_____ **pajitas de beber**
_____ **palillos de dientes**

# School-Home Connection

Harcourt Science

## Chapter Content

Today we begin a new chapter in science. Your child will be learning about the seasons. We will be doing science activities that investigate the best season to sprout seeds, colors and fabrics that help to keep children cool and warm in different seasons, and how some animals store food for the winter.

## Science Process Skills

Learning to **predict** is an important skill of science. A scientific prediction is made once a pattern has been observed. Children are asked to think about previous observations before making predictions.

Show your child a seed. Have your child use past observations to predict the stages the plant will go through as it grows from a seed to a mature plant. Talk about how different climates might affect the growth of the plant. If possible, plant the seed and compare its growth to the predictions you made together.

## Science Fun

Help your child select a part of the country or world with seasonal changes different from those you experience in your area. Use library resources to find out about the climate in the area you chose. Your child may wish to make a collage or poster showing what people do differently there because of the climate.

***Dear Rebecca, Winter is Here*** by Jean Craighead George (Harpercollins Juvenile Books, 1993).

Your child may enjoy learning about the changing seasons in *Dear Rebecca, Winter is Here,* by Jean Craighead George. In this story, an elderly woman writes to her granddaughter about the changes that take place in nature when winter comes.

## Activity Materials from Home

Dear Family Member:

To do the activities in this chapter, we will need some materials that you may have around the house. Please note the items listed at the right. If possible, please send these things to school with your child.

Your help and support are appreciated!

- ____ **apples**
- ____ **string**
- ____ **zip-top bags**
- ____ **scraps of wool**
- ____ **cotton balls**
- ____ **Styrofoam "peanuts"**
- ____ **newspaper**

# La escuela y la casa

**Harcourt Ciencias**

## Contenido del capítulo

Hoy comenzamos un nuevo capítulo de ciencias. Su hijo(a) aprenderá sobre las estaciones del año. Realizaremos actividades científicas que investigan la mejor temporada para que broten las semillas, los colores y las telas que ayudan a los niños a mantenerse frescos y cálidos en temporadas diferentes y cómo algunos animales guardan comida en el invierno.

## Destrezas del proceso científico

Aprender a **predecir** es una destreza importante de las ciencias. Una predicción científica se realiza una vez que se ha observado un patrón. A los niños se les pide que piensen sobre observaciones previas antes de hacer predicciones.

Muéstrele a su hijo(a) una semilla. Pida a su hijo(a) que use las observaciones pasadas para predecir las etapas por la que pasará la planta a medida que se convierte de una semilla hasta una planta madura. Hable sobre cómo los diferentes climas podrían afectar el crecimiento de la planta. Si es posible, siembre la semilla y compare su crecimiento con las predicciones que hicieron juntos.

## Diversión

Ayude a su hijo(a) a seleccionar una parte del país o del mundo con diferentes cambios de estaciones como las que ha experimentado en su área. Use los recursos de la biblioteca para descubrir los climas en el área que eligió. Su hijo(a) quizás desee hacer un collage o cartel que muestre lo que hacen las personas diferente allí debido al clima.

*Dear Rebecca, Winter is Here* de Jean Craighead George (Harpercollins Juvenile Books, 1993).

Quizás su hijo(a) se divierta aprendiendo sobre las estaciones del año en *Dear Rebecca, Winter is Here* de Jean Craighead George. En esta historia, una mujer mayor le escribe a su nieta sobre los cambios que suceden en la naturaleza cuando llega el invierno.

## Materiales de casa para la actividad

Querido familiar:

Para hacer las actividades en este capítulo, necesitaremos algunos materiales que tal vez tenga en la casa. Observe los artículos de la lista de la derecha. Si es posible, por favor envíe estas cosas con su hijo(a) a la escuela.

¡Gracias por su ayuda y su apoyo!

____ **manzanas**
____ **hilo**
____ **bolsas de plástico con cierre**
____ **pedacitos de lana**
____ **bolitas de algodón**
____ **bolitas de espuma de estireno**
____ **periódico**

# School-Home Connection

Harcourt Science

## Chapter Content

Today we begin a new chapter in science about matter. Your child will be learning about solids, liquids, and gases. We will do activities that explore the properties of solids, liquids, and gases. We will also investigate what makes objects float or sink. We will finish the chapter by learning how we can change matter.

## Science Process Skills

Learning to **gather and record data** is an important skill in science. To encourage your child to practice gathering and recording data, find objects around the house that can either sink or float. Sinking and floating are physical properties of matter. Have your child predict whether each object will sink or float. Help your child record his or her predictions. Then test the objects and record what you observed. Help your child understand that recording data makes it easier to remember what has happened and talk about observations with others. It also aids in drawing conclusions about what has been observed.

## Science Fun

Matter has different physical properties.

### Candy Creatures

**What You Need**

- assorted candies, gum drops, chocolate chips, marshmallows, licorice string, and candy corn
- icing to use as a "glue"

**What to Do**

1. Help your child examine the different candies. Talk about the properties of the candies.
2. Explain that you will be making candy creatures. Work together to choose candies that would make good arms, legs, bodies, faces, and so on.
3. Construct as many creatures as you can design. Examples might be spiders or other bugs, animals, and so on. Use the icing to "glue" the different parts together.
4. Share your creatures with the rest of your family.

## Activity Materials from Home

Dear Family Member:

To do the activities in this chapter, we will need some materials that you may have around the house. Please note the items at the right. If possible, please send these things to school with your child.

Your help and support are appreciated!

____ **objects such as a rock, red marble, piece of yellow fabric**
____ **different-size plastic containers**
____ **balloon**
____ **plastic soft drink bottle**

# La escuela y la casa

Harcourt Ciencias

## Contenido del capítulo

Hoy comenzamos un nuevo capítulo de ciencias. Su hijo(a) aprenderá sobre la materia, los sólidos, los líquidos y los gases. Realizaremos actividades científicas que exploran las propiedades de los sólidos, los líquidos y los gases, qué hace que los objetos floten o se hundan y cómo podemos cambiar la materia.

## Destrezas del proceso científico

Aprender a **recopilar y anotar datos** es una destreza importante de las ciencias. Para animar a su hijo(a) a practicar a recopilar y anotar datos, busque objetos en su casa que puedan flotar o hundirse. Hundir y flotar son propiedades físicas de una materia. Pida a su hijo que prediga si cada uno de los objetos se hundirá o flotará. Ayude a su hijo(a) a anotar sus predicciones. Luego pruebe los objetos y anote lo que observó. Ayude a su hijo(a) a comprender que anotar datos hace más fácil recordar lo que ha pasado y hablar de las observaciones con otros. Esto también ayuda a sacar conclusiones de lo que se ha observado.

## Diversión

La materia tiene propiedades físicas diferentes.

### Criaturas de dulce

**Lo que necesitas**

- caramelos surtidos, gomitas, trocitos de chocolate, dulce de malvavisco y dulce de regaliz
- glaseado para usar como "pegamento"

**Lo que vas a hacer**

1. Ayude a su hijo(a) a examinar los diferentes caramelos. Hable sobre las propiedades de los caramelos.
2. Explique que harán criaturas de dulce. Trabajen para elegir caramelos que formarán buenos brazos, piernas, cuerpos, caras y así sucesivamente.
3. Construyan tantas criaturas como las que puedan diseñar. Los ejemplos pueden ser arañas u otros insectos, animales y así sucesivamente. Usen el glaseado para "pegar" las diferentes partes.
4. Compartan sus criaturas con el resto de la familia.

## Materiales de casa para la actividad

Querido familiar:

Para hacer las actividades en este capítulo, necesitaremos algunos materiales que tal vez tenga en la casa. Observe los artículos de la lista de la derecha. Si es posible, por favor envíe estas cosas con su hijo(a) a la escuela.

¡Gracias por su ayuda y su apoyo!

____ **objetos como una roca, una canica roja, un pedazo de tela amarilla**
____ **diferentes tamaños de recipientes de plástico**
____ **globo**
____ **botella de refresco de plástico**

# School-Home Connection

Harcourt Science

## Chapter Content

Today we begin a new chapter in science. Your child will be learning about some properties of heat and light. We will be doing activities that measure temperature and observe how heat changes matter. We will also study how light reflects and refracts.

## Science Process Skills

Learning to **communicate** is an important science skill. To encourage your child to communicate clearly about his or her ideas, talk with your child about shadows. You or your child can use a blank wall, a flashlight, and a few common objects from around the house to make shadows. Take turns guessing and discussing what each object is. Then try making shadow puppets with your hands. Have your child talk about how the shadows are made. (The solid object between the flashlight and the wall blocks the light, forming a shadow.)

## Science Fun

Removing heat from liquids causes them to freeze solid.

### Fun Ice Cubes

**What You Need**

- water
- seltzer water
- cups
- ice cube tray
- food coloring
- rubber bands
- small molds or small zip-top bags

**What to Do**

1. Add several drops of food coloring to four cups of water or clear seltzer water.
2. Pour the colored liquid into the ice cube trays or molds. Freeze.
3. For crazy ice, pour the colored water into small zip-top bags. Carefully press as much air as possible out of the bag, and then seal. Use rubber bands to form the bags into different shapes.
4. Freeze until ready to use.

## Activity Materials from Home

Dear Family Member:

To do the activities in this chapter, we will need some materials that you may have around the house. Please note the items listed at the right. If possible, please send these things to school with your child.

Your help and support are appreciated!

____ **plastic cups**
____ **food coloring**
____ **small mirror**

# La escuela y la casa

**Harcourt Ciencias**

## Contenido del capítulo

Hoy comenzamos un nuevo capítulo de ciencias. Su hijo(a) aprenderá sobre algunas propiedades del calor y de la luz. Realizaremos actividades científicas que miden la temperatura y observan cómo el calor cambia la materia. También estudiaremos cómo la luz se refleja y se refracta.

## Destrezas del proceso científico

Aprender a **comunicar** es una destreza importante de las ciencias. Para animar a su hijo(a) a comunicar claramente sus ideas, hable con su hijo(a) sobre las sombras. Ud. o su hijo(a) puede usar una pared en blanco, una linterna y algunos objetos comunes de la casa que formen sombras. Túrnense adivinando y comentando qué es cada objeto. Luego traten de formar sombras de mascotas con sus manos. Pida a su hijo(a) que hable sobre cómo se forman las sombras. (El objeto sólido entre la linterna y la pared bloquea la luz, formando una sombra.)

## Diversión

Quitarle el calor a los líquidos hace que se congelen.

### Cubos de hielo divertidos

**Lo que necesitas**

- agua
- agua mineral
- vasos
- bandeja de cubos de hielo
- colorante
- elásticos
- moldes pequeños o bolsas pequeñas con cierre

**Lo que vas a hacer**

1. Agrega algunas gotas de colorante a cuatro vasos de agua o agua mineral.
2. Coloca el líquido con color en la bandeja de cubos de hielo o en los moldes. Congela.
3. Para hacer hielo con formas, coloca el agua con color en las bolsas pequeñas con cierre. Presiona con cuidado para sacar la mayor cantidad de aire de la bolsa y luego sellar. Usa los elásticos para darle diferentes formas a la bolsa.
4. Congela hasta que se pueda usar.

## Materiales de casa para la actividad

Querido familiar:

Para hacer las actividades de este capítulo, necesitaremos algunos materiales que tal vez tenga alrededor de la casa. Observe los artículos de la lista de la derecha. Si es posible, por favor envíe estas cosas con su hijo(a) a la escuela.

¡Gracias por su ayuda y apoyo!

_____ **vasos de plástico**
_____ **colorante**
_____ **espejo pequeño**

# School-Home Connection

Harcourt Science

## Chapter Content

Today we begin a new chapter in science. Your child will be learning about what makes things move. We will be doing many activities, including investigating what will make something move, grouping objects that move the same way, and predicting how an object might change its motion.

## Science Process Skills

**Prediction** is an important science skill. Scientific predictions are based on observations and inferences about those observations. You can help your child practice making predictions.

With your child, observe moving objects such as toys or vehicles in and around your home. After watching these objects, have your child predict things such as how far or fast something might travel or how long a toy might move. If you make the Come-Back Can described under *Science Fun*, try rolling the cans at different speeds and having your child predict what will happen.

## Science Fun

Make a toy that seems to move by itself!

### Come-Back Can

**What You Need**

- coffee can with ends removed (tape over sharp edges)
- 2 plastic lids that fit the can
- long rubber band
- scissors
- fishing weight
- 2 toothpicks

**What to Do**

1. Have an adult use scissors to punch a hole in each can lid (center).
2. Push one end of the rubber band through the hole from the inside and secure it over a toothpick. Thread the weight through the rubber band. Snap the lid on one end of the can. Attach the other end of the rubber band to the second lid and snap on the can.
3. Roll the can away from you. Observe what happens.

## Activity Materials from Home

Dear Family Member:

To do the activities in this chapter, we will need some materials that you might have around the house. Please note the items at the right. If possible, please send these things to school with your child.

Your help and support are appreciated!

____ **plastic straws**
____ **craft sticks**
____ **rubber bands**
____ **string**
____ **plastic egg**
____ **toilet paper roll**

# La escuela y la casa

**Harcourt Ciencias**

## Contenido del capítulo

Hoy comenzamos un nuevo capítulo de ciencias. Su hijo(a) aprenderá qué hace que las cosas se muevan. Realizaremos actividades científicas para investigar qué hace que algo se mueva, agrupar objetos que se mueven en la misma dirección y predecir cómo un objeto podría cambiar su dirección.

## Destrezas del proceso científico

**Predecir** es una destreza importante de las ciencias. Las predicciones científicas son basadas en observaciones e inferencias sobre esas observaciones. Ud. puede ayudar a su hijo(a) a practicar a hacer predicciones.

Con su hijo(a), observe objetos como juguetes o vehículos de su casa y su alrededor. Después de observar estos objetos, pida a su hijo(a) que prediga cosas como qué tan lejos o rápido puede ir algo o por cuánto tiempo se moverá un juguete. Si hace la Lata que se devuelve descrita en la sección de *Diversión,* trate de rodar los envases a velocidades diferentes y pida a su hijo(a) que prediga lo que pasará.

## Diversión

¡Hacer un juguete que parece moverse por sí mismo!

### La lata que se devuelve

**Lo que necesitas**

- una lata de café sin fondo (colocar cinta adhesiva a los bordes afilados)
- 2 tapas de plástico que le sirvan a la lata
- elástico grande
- tijeras
- plomos de pescar
- 2 palillos de dientes

**Lo que vas a hacer**

1. Pide a un adulto que use las tijeras para hacer un hueco en cada tapa del envase (en el centro).
2. Empuja una de las puntas del elástico por dentro a través del agujero de una de las tapas y asegúralo con un palillo de dientes. Inserta el plomo a través del elástico. Ata la otra punta del elástico a la otra tapa y sujétala a la tapa.
3. Rueda la lata lejos de ti. Observa qué sucede.

## Materiales de casa para la actividad

Querido familiar:

Para hacer las actividades de este capítulo, necesitaremos algunos materiales que tal vez tenga en la casa. Observe los artículos de la lista de la derecha. Si es posible, por favor envíe estas cosas con su hijo(a) a la escuela.

¡Gracias por su ayuda y apoyo!

_____ **pajitas plásticas**
_____ **palitos**
_____ **elásticos**
_____ **hilo**
_____ **huevo de plástico**
_____ **rollo de papel de baño**

# School-Home Connection

Harcourt Science

## Chapter Content

Today we begin a new chapter in science. Your child will learn about magnets. We will be doing activities that help us understand what a magnet can do, where the poles of a magnet are located, and the types of things that can be magnetized.

## Science Process Skills

Learning to **draw conclusions** is an important skill in science. Drawing conclusions is done after observations are made. Drawing conclusions based on observation is how we make sense of the world around us.

To give your child practice in making observations and drawing conclusions from those observations, observe and experiment with magnets around the house. Give your child an assortment of objects, such as paper clips, pencils, and various types of hardware. Make sure that some of the materials will be attracted to a magnet, and others won't. Have your child test the different objects, and observe what happens. Then help your child draw a conclusion about what types of things are attracted to magnets. (The objects that are attracted to a magnet contain the metal iron.)

## Science Fun

### Picture Magnets

**What You Need**

- strip of magnetic tape
- favorite photo
- glue
- cardboard
- cookie cutter
- scissors

**What to Do**

1. Trace the shape of the cookie cutter onto the cardboard and the photo, making sure to include the part of the photo you want on your finished magnet.
2. Cut out both shapes.
3. Glue the photo to the cardboard.
4. Glue the strip of magnetic tape to the back of the cardboard. Let dry.
5. Use your magnet to decorate the refrigerator or give to a friend!

## Activity Materials from Home

Dear Family Member:

To do the activities in this chapter, we will need some materials that you may have around the house. Please note the items listed at the right. If possible, please send these things to school with your child.

Your help and support are appreciated!

____ **small objects such as buttons, barrettes, nails, marbles, balls, and jacks**
____ **piece of carpet**
____ **cardboard box**

# La escuela y la casa

Harcourt Ciencias

## Contenido del capítulo

Hoy comenzamos un nuevo capítulo de ciencias. Su hijo(a) aprenderá sobre los imanes. Realizaremos actividades científicas que ayudarán a comprender qué puede hacer un imán, dónde se encuentran ubicados los polos de los imanes y los tipos de cosas que se pueden magnetizar.

## Destrezas del proceso científico

Aprender a **sacar conclusiones** es una destreza importante de las ciencias. Sacar conclusiones se hace después de que se han hecho las observaciones. Sacar conclusiones basadas en una observación es como le damos sentido al mundo que nos rodea.

Para hacer que su hijo(a) practique observar y sacar conclusiones de estas observaciones, observe y experimente con imanes en su casa. Dele a su hijo(a) una serie de objetos como clips, lápices y varios tipos de objetos metálicos. Asegúrese de que algunos de estos materiales serán atraídos por el imán y otros no. Pida a su hijo(a) que pruebe los diferentes objetos y observe qué sucede. Luego ayude a su hijo(a) a sacar una conclusión sobre qué tipo de cosas son atraídas por los imanes. (Los objetos que son atraídos por un imán contienen el metal hierro.)

## Diversión

### Imanes de fotografías

**Lo que necesitas**

- tira de cinta adhesiva magnética
- fotografía favorita
- pegamento
- cartulina
- cortador de galletas
- tijeras

**Lo que vas a hacer**

1. Traza la figura del cortador de galletas en la cartulina y en la fotografía asegurándote de incluir la parte de la fotografía que quieres cuando termines tu imán.
2. Corta ambas figuras.
3. Pega la fotografía en la cartulina.
4. Pega la tira de cinta adhesiva magnética en la parte trasera de la cartulina. Deja secar.
5. Usa tu imán para decorar el refrigerador o dárselo a un amigo.

## Materiales de casa para la actividad

Querido familiar:

Para hacer las actividades en este capítulo, necesitaremos algunos materiales que tal vez tenga en la casa. Observe los artículos de la lista de la derecha. Si es posible, por favor envíe estas cosas con su hijo(a) a la escuela.

¡Gracias por su ayuda y su apoyo!

____ **objetos pequeños como botones, hebillas, clavos, canicas, pelotas y matatenas**
____ **pedazos de alfombra**
____ **caja de cartulina**

Name ______________________ Date ______________

# How Do My Senses Help Me Learn?

## Investigate

## Using Your Senses

**You will need**

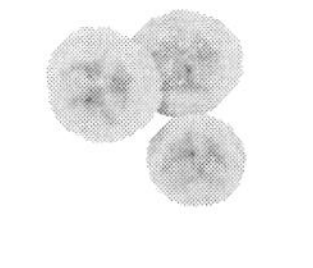
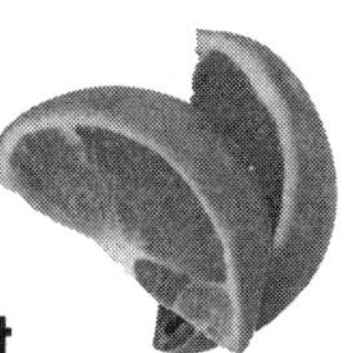

pieces of fruit

plastic gloves

1. Close your eyes. Your partner will put on gloves and give you a piece of fruit.

2. Touch and smell the fruit. Tell what you observe. Name the fruit.

3. Take turns with your partner.

**Science Skill**
When you observe things, use more than your eyes to find out about them.

Name ______________________ Date ______________

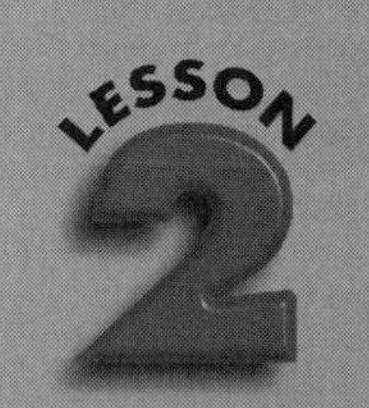


# What Are Living and Nonliving Things?

## Investigate

## A Mealworm and a Rock

**You will need**

mealworm

rock

hand lens

bran meal

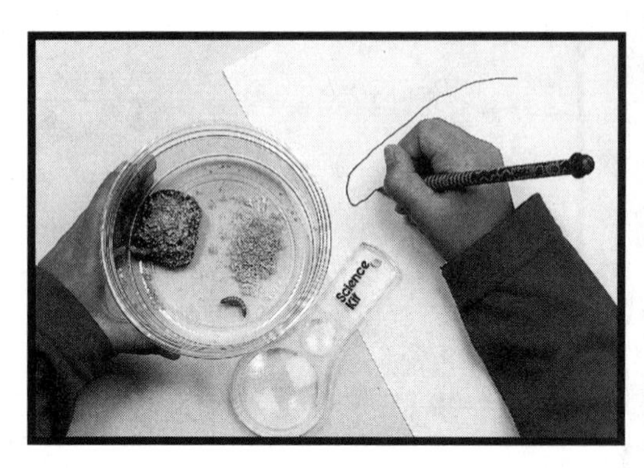


1. Give bran meal to the mealworm and the rock. Use the hand lens to observe.
2. Does the mealworm or the rock move or eat? Draw what you see.
3. Compare the mealworm and the rock. Which is a living thing?

**Science Skill**
When you compare things, you tell how they are the same and different.

A10

Harcourt

Name ______________________ Date ______________

# What Are the Parts of a Plant?

**Investigate**

## Plant Parts

**You will need**

carrot

plant with flower

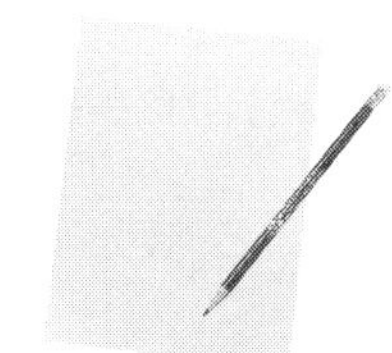

paper and pencil

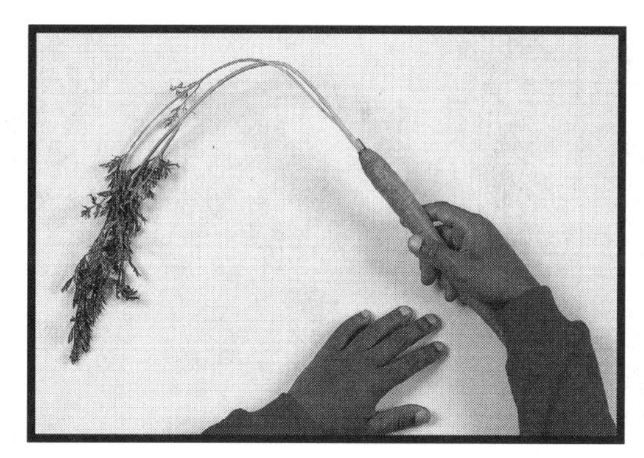

1. Look at the parts of one plant. Draw what you see.
2. Look at the parts of the other plant. Draw what you see.
3. Compare the plants. Tell about their parts.

**Science Skill**

When you compare things, you tell how they are the same and different.

Name ______________________ Date ______________

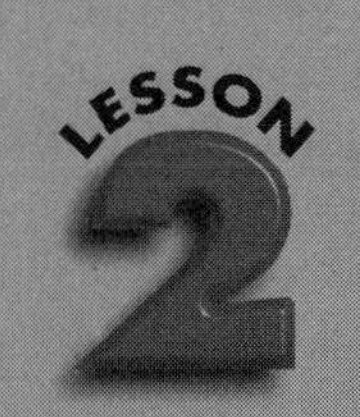

# How Do Plants Grow?

## The Inside of a Seed

**You will need**

bean seed

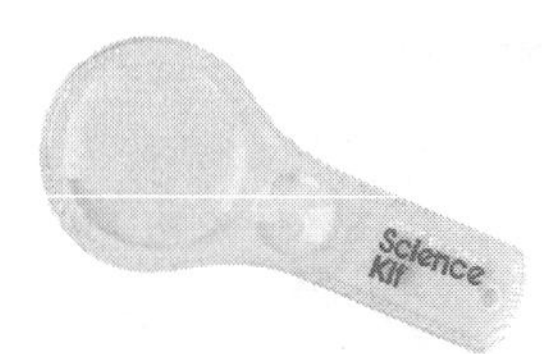


hand lens

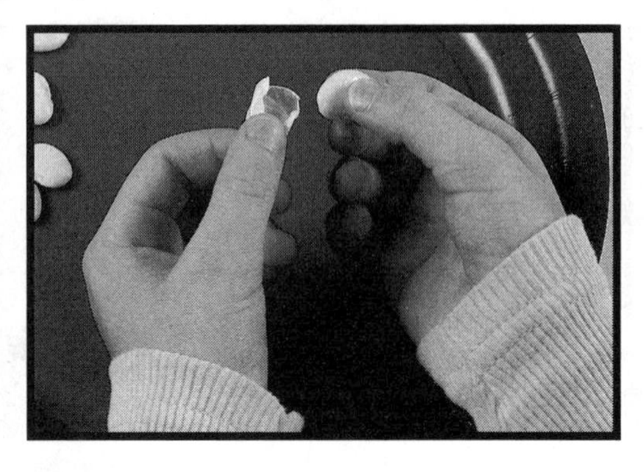

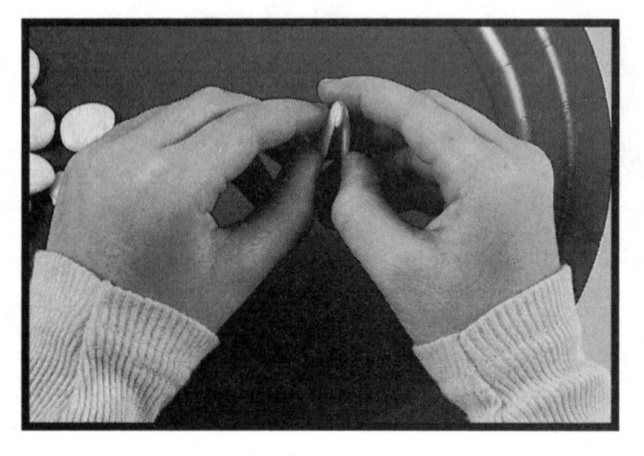

1. Peel off the covering of the seed.
2. Open the seed.
3. Observe. Tell what is inside.

**Science Skill**
Use a hand lens to help you observe.

A28

Harcourt



Use with page A28.

Name ______________________ Date ______________

# What Do Plants Need?

## Investigate

## What Plants Need to Grow

**You will need**

seeds

2 clear cups

any color cup

soil

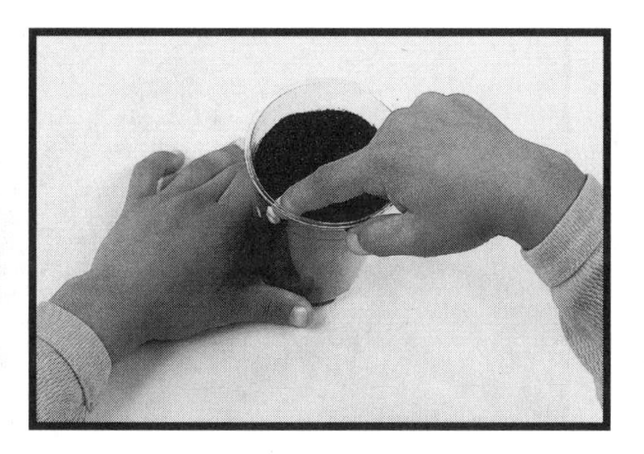

1. Fill one clear cup with soil. Plant two seeds near the side. Water.
2. Put the cup with the seeds into the cup with color. After 3 days, take it out.
3. Share what you see.

**Science Skill**
When you share your ideas, you communicate with others.

A32

Name ______________________ Date ______________

# What Do Animals Need?

## Investigate

## An Animal Home

**You will need**

plastic box and gloves

soil, twig, and rocks

water in a bottle cap

small animals

1. Put the soil, twig, rocks, water, and animals in the box.
2. Observe. How does your home give the animals food, water, and a place to hide?
3. Draw what you see. Close the lid.

**Science Skill**
When you observe the animals in their home, you can see how they meet their needs.

A42





Use with page A42.

Name ______________________ Date ______________

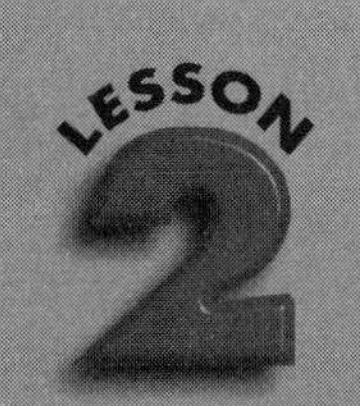


# What Are Some Kinds of Animals?

**Investigate**

## Animals in Your Neighborhood

**You will need**

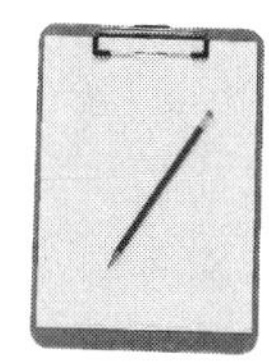

paper and pencil

1. Observe different kinds of animals in your schoolyard.
2. Draw a picture of each animal you observe.
3. Classify the animals into groups. How are the animals in each group the same?

**Science Skill**
When you classify animals, you observe how they are the same. Then you group them.

A48

Name ______________________ Date ______________

# What Are Insects?

## Investigate

## A Model of an Insect

**You will need**

Styrofoam balls

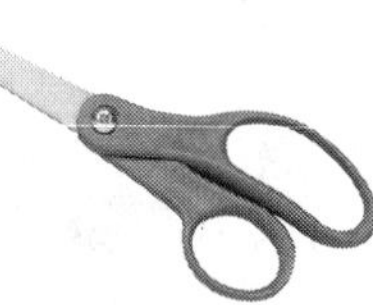

scissors

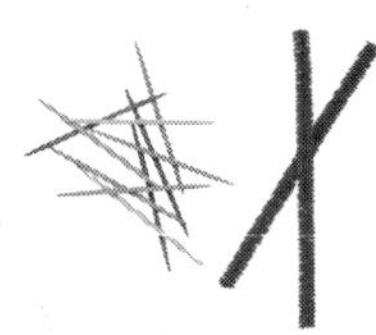

toothpicks and chenille sticks

wax paper

1. Choose an insect to make. Insects have three body parts and six legs.
2. Choose materials. Make a model of your insect.
   CAUTION Be careful with toothpicks, chenille sticks, and scissors. They are sharp.

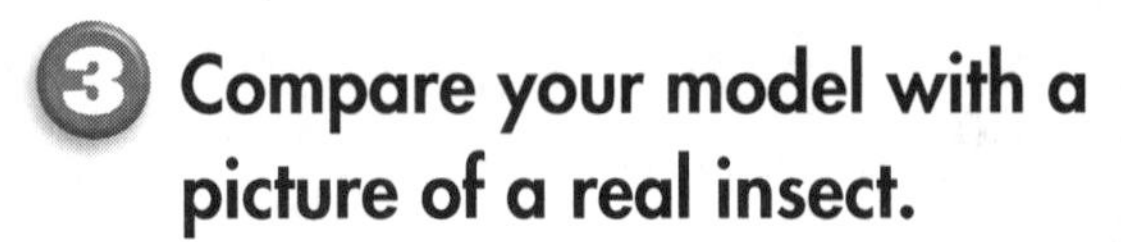

3. Compare your model with a picture of a real insect.

**Science Skill**

When you make a model of an insect, you show parts that a real insect has.

A54

Name ______________________ Date ______________

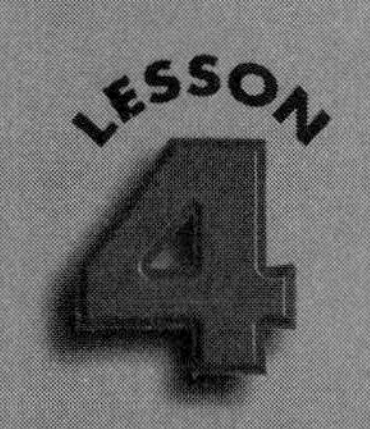


# How Do Animals Grow?

**Investigate**

## Animals and Their Young

**You will need**

animal picture cards

paper and pencil

| Animals and Their Young | | |
|---|---|---|
| Animal | Same | Different |
| cats | Both have ears. Both are orange. | One is big. One is small. |
| | | |
| | | |
| | | |
| | | |

1. Match the picture cards. Put each young animal with the adult.
2. Make a chart. Compare the young animal and the adult.
3. Tell how each young animal is like the adult. Tell how it is different.

**Science Skill**

When you compare the pictures, you tell how they are the same and different.

A58

Name ______________________ Date ______________

# How Does a Butterfly Grow?

## Investigate

## A Butterfly's Life

**You will need**

box

caterpillar

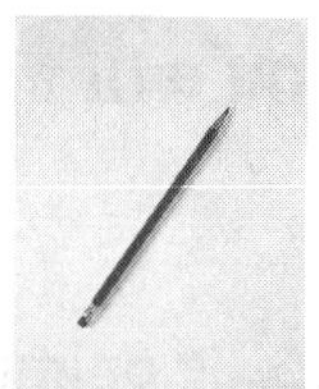
paper and pencil

1. Keep your caterpillar in a warm place.
2. Observe your caterpillar for three weeks. Draw it each time.
3. How did your caterpillar change? Share what happened.

**Science Skill**
When you use your senses to observe, you find out how the caterpillar changes.

A64





Use with page A64.

Name ____________________ Date ____________________

# How Does a Frog Grow?

## Investigate

## A Frog's Life

**You will need**

picture cards

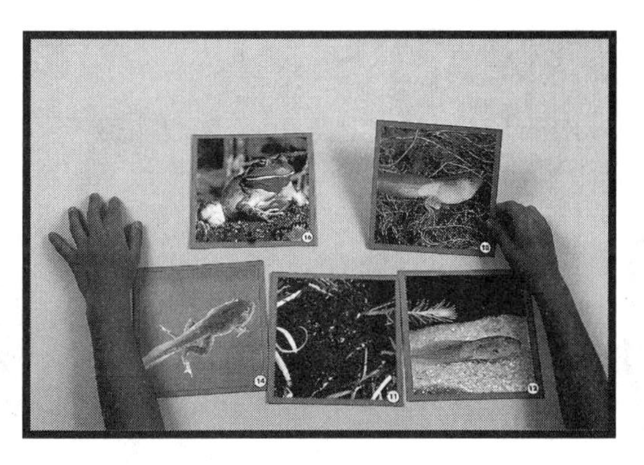

1. Put the picture cards in sequence. Show how you think a frog changes as it grows.

2. Tell why you put your cards in the order you did.

**Science Skill**

When you sequence the cards, you show what happens first, next, and last.

**A70**

Harcourt

Name ______________________ Date ______________

# How Do Animals Need Plants?

**Investigate**

## How Small Animals Use Plants

**You will need**

timer or watch

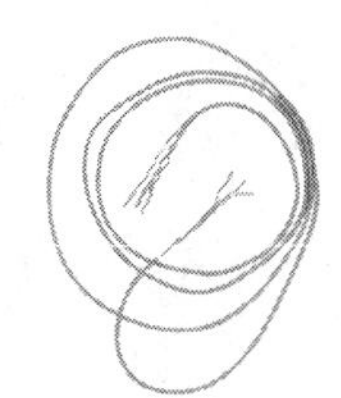
string loop

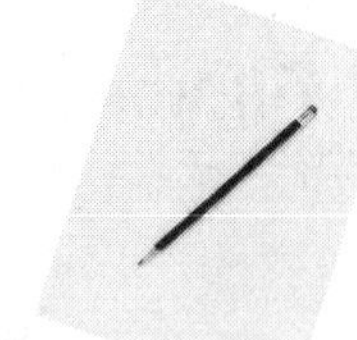
paper and pencil

1. Go outside with your class. Observe animals and plants inside your string loop.
2. Observe and record for five minutes. How are animals using plants?
3. Share what you observed.

**Science Skill**

As you observe, use your senses of sight, hearing, and smell to help you.

Name ______________________ Date ______________

# How Do Animals Help Plants?

## Investigate

## How Seeds Stick to Animals

**You will need**

Styrofoam ball

glue

cotton and other materials to try out

1. Look at this picture. How might these seeds stick to animals?
2. Plan a model of a seed that sticks. Choose materials to glue to the ball.
3. Investigate your materials. Which ones stick to the cotton? The cotton is like animal fur.

**Science Skill**

To investigate how seeds stick to animals, make a plan to try out different ideas. Follow your plan.

B10

Name ______________________ Date ______________

# How Do We Need Plants and Animals?

## Investigate

## Things People Use

**You will need**

picture cards

1. Which pictures show things made from plants? Which are from animals?
2. Classify the cards. Sort them into groups.
3. Share your groups. Tell why each thing belongs.

**Science Skill**
When you classify the things on the cards, you group them to show ways they are the same.

B14





Use with page B14.

Name ______________________ Date ______________

# What Lives in a Forest?

## Investigate

## Forest Trees

**You will need**

dark crayon

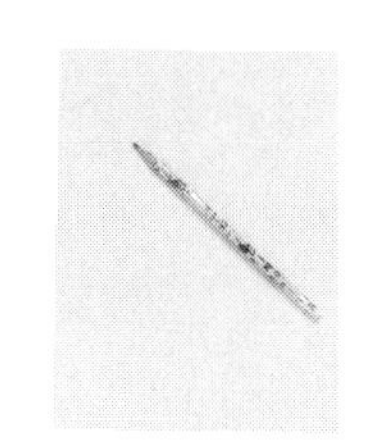

pencil and paper

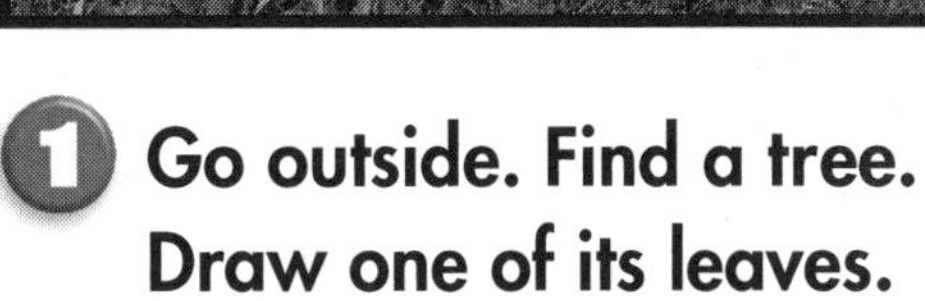

1. Go outside. Find a tree. Draw one of its leaves.
2. Make a rubbing of the tree's bark.
3. Compare your drawing and rubbing with a classmate's.

**Science Skill**

When you compare drawings and rubbings, look for ways the trees are the same and different.

Name ______________________ Date ______________

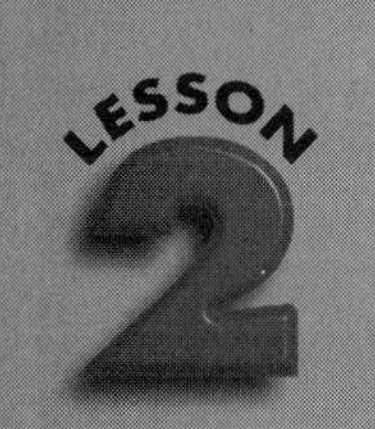


# What Lives in the Desert?

## Investigate

## Desert Leaves

**You will need**

2 paper clips

water

wax paper

2 paper-towel leaf shapes

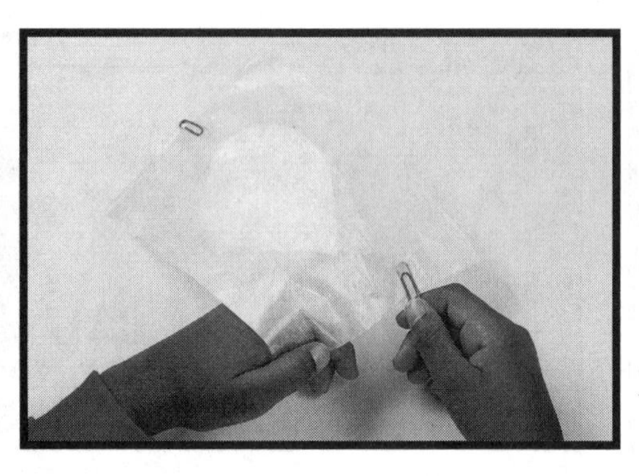

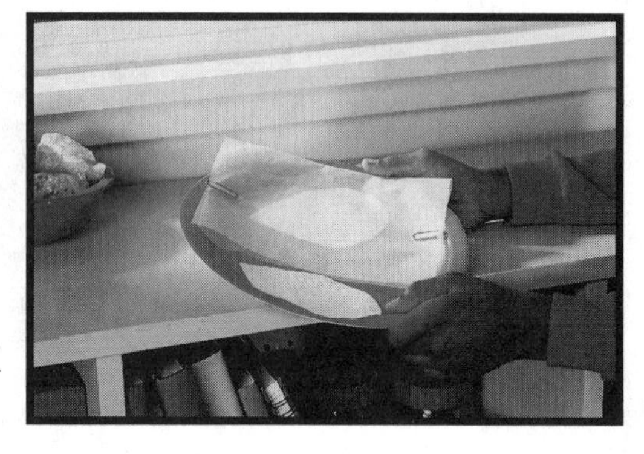

1. Make both leaf shapes damp. Put one shape on wax paper. Fold the paper over. Clip it.
2. Put both leaves in the sunlight. Check them after an hour.
3. Which leaf holds water longer? Draw a conclusion.

**Science Skill**

To draw a conclusion about desert leaves, think about your leaf with the waxy coat and the other leaf.

B30

Name ______________________ Date ______________

# What Lives in a Rain Forest?

## Investigate

## Rain Forest Plants

**You will need**

seeds

2 wet cotton balls

film cans and lid with hole

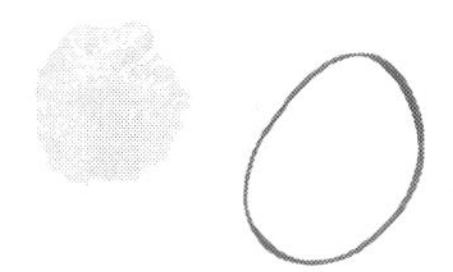

plastic and band

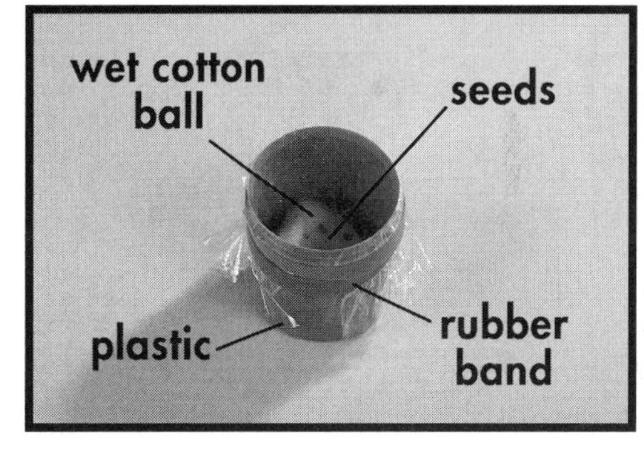


1. Rain forest plants get little light. Make a model of a rain forest like this one. Close lid.
2. Open forest plants get more light. Make an open forest like this one.
3. Set both models in the sun for 5 days. Tell how the cotton changes.

**Science Skill**

To communicate how the forests grew, draw and share pictures of what you observed.

Name ____________________ Date ____________

# What Lives in the Ocean?

**Investigate**

## Ocean Animals

**You will need**

ocean picture cards

1. Which ocean pictures show fish? Which show other animals?
2. Classify the animals. Put them in groups.
3. Share your groups. Talk about other ways to classify the animals.

**Science Skill**
When you classify the animals, you group them to show ways they are the same.

B38





Use with page B38.

Name ______________________ Date ______________

# What Can We Observe About Rocks?

## Investigate

## Ways to Classify Rocks

**You will need**

hand lens

different rocks

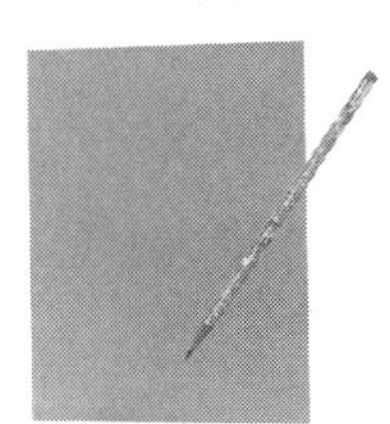

paper and pencil

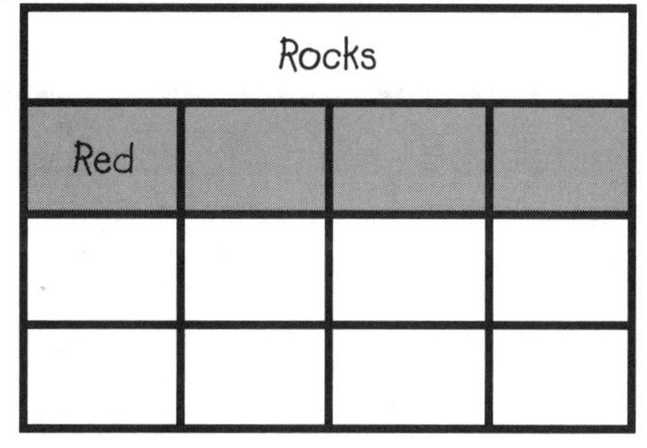

| Rocks | | | |
|---|---|---|---|
| Red | | | |
| | | | |
| | | | |

1. Observe each rock with the hand lens. Feel each rock. Write how the rocks look and feel.
2. Make a chart. Classify your rocks on the chart.

**Science Skill**
When you classify your rocks, you group them by ways they are the same.

C4

Name ______________________ Date ______________

# What Is Soil?

**Investigate**

## Observing Soil

**You will need**

soil

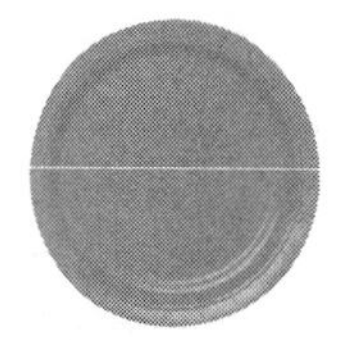

paper plate

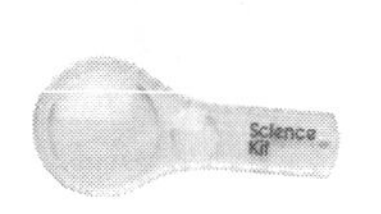


hand lens

paper and pencil

| Soil | | |
|---|---|---|
| Looks | Smells | Feels |
| | | |

1. Make a chart like this one. Then observe the soil with a hand lens. Move the soil around.
2. Smell and feel the soil. Think of words that tell about it.
3. Draw pictures and write words that tell about the soil.

**Science Skill**
When you observe the soil, use your senses to find out how it looks, smells, and feels.

C8





Use with page C8.

Name ______________________ Date ______________

# How Do Different Soils Compare?

## Investigate

## How Soils Compare

**You will need**

hand lens

3 kinds of soil

paper plate

spoon

1. Observe each kind of soil. How does it smell and feel?
2. Put some of each soil on the plate. Use the hand lens to observe.
3. Compare the three kinds of soil. Tell your classmates about them.

**Science Skill**
When you compare the soils, you tell how they are the same and different.

C12

Name ______________________ Date ______________

# Where Is Air on Earth?

## Investigate

## Air in a Bag

**You will need**

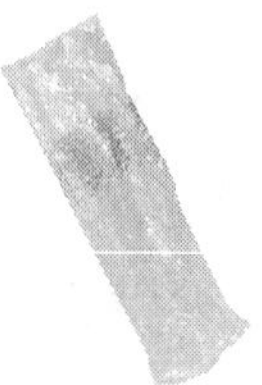

plastic bag

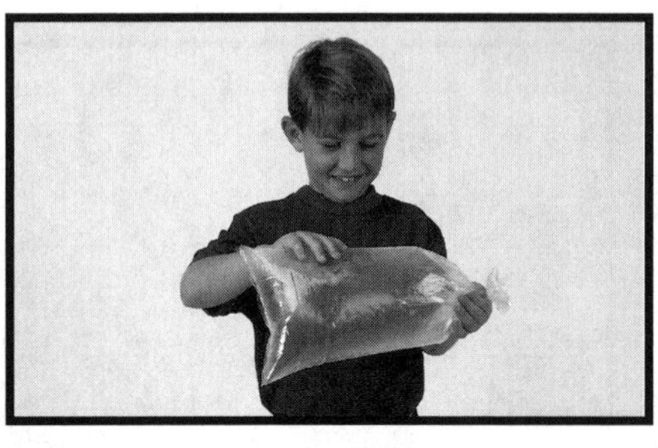

1. Pull an open bag toward you. Then hold the top of the bag closed.
2. Squeeze the bag. What do you observe? Poke a hole in the bag.
3. What was in the bag? How did you infer that?

**Science Skill**
When you infer, you use what you observe and know to make a good guess.

Name ______________________ Date ______________

# Where Is Fresh Water Found?

Investigate

## Making Salt Water Fresh

**You will need**

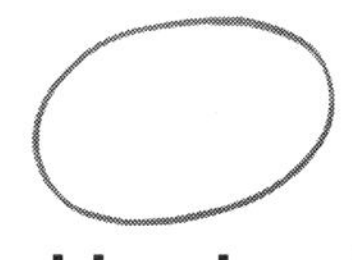

rubber band

bucket and sand

marbles and plastic wrap

2 cups

1. Mix some salt in water. Taste the water. Pour the water into the bucket. Throw away used cups.
2. Put another cup in the bottom of the bucket. Cover. Put marbles on top.
3. Place bucket in the sun. Wait two hours. Take the cup out. Taste the water. Draw a conclusion.

**Science Skill**

To draw a conclusion, think about what you observed and what you know about water.

Name ______________________ Date ______________

# Where Is Salt Water on Earth?

## Investigate

## Salt and Salt Water

**You will need**

hand lens

salt and spoon

cup of water

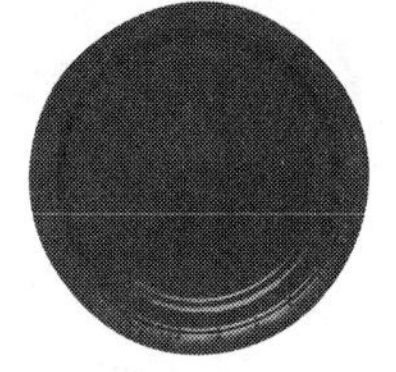
plate

1. Observe salt on a plate. Draw or write about it.
2. Stir the salt into the water until you can not see it. Write about it.
3. Put some salt water on the plate. Leave it all night. Then communicate what is left on the plate.

**Science Skill**
When you communicate, use your writing to help you tell others what you observed.

Name ______________________ Date ______________

# What Is Weather?

## Investigate

## Weather Conditions

You will need

paper

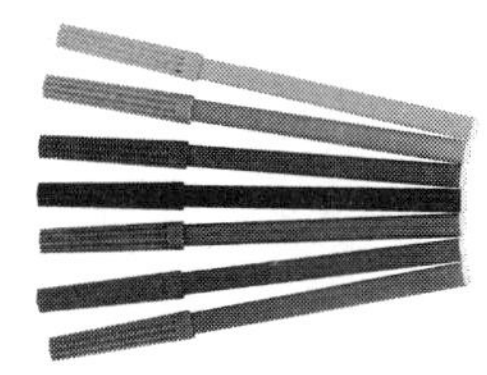

markers

1. Observe the changes in weather.
2. Draw or write what you observe.
3. Compare observations with a classmate. Add your page to a class book.

**Science Skill**
When you compare the things you observed, tell how they are the same and different.

Name ______________________ Date ______________

# What Is Temperature?

## Investigate

## Measuring Air Temperature

**You will need**

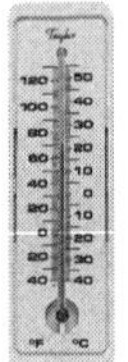

thermometer

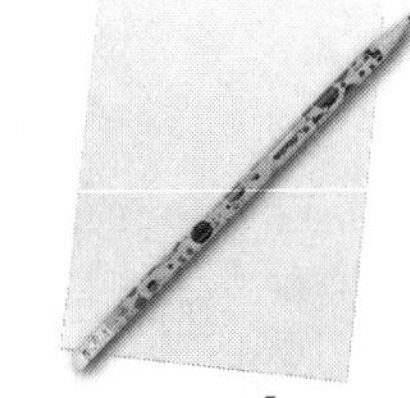

paper and pencil

red crayon

1. Draw and label two thermometers.
2. Measure and record the air temperature in the classroom.
3. Put the thermometer outside for 5 minutes. Measure and record the air temperature.
4. Compare the temperatures.

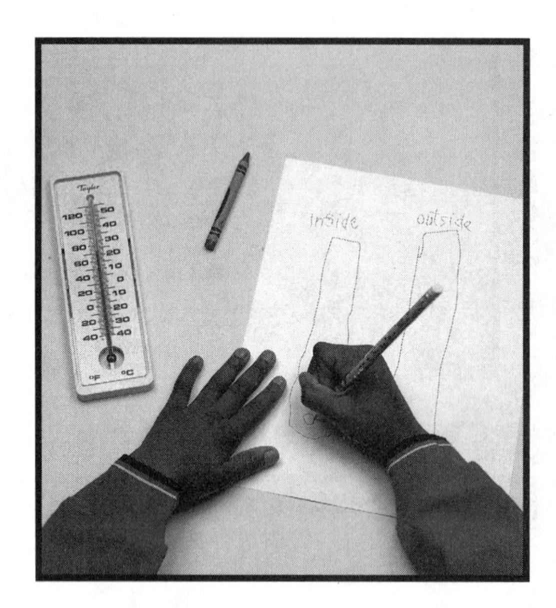


**Science Skill**

To measure temperature with a thermometer, read the number next to the top of the red line.

D8

Harcourt

Name ______________________ Date ______________

# What Is Wind?

## Investigate

## Wind Direction

**You will need**

drinking straw

round toothpick

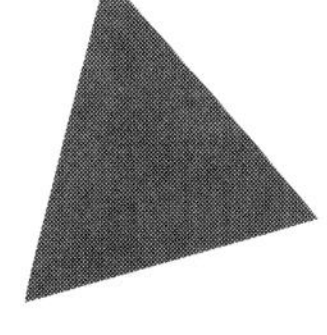
paper triangle

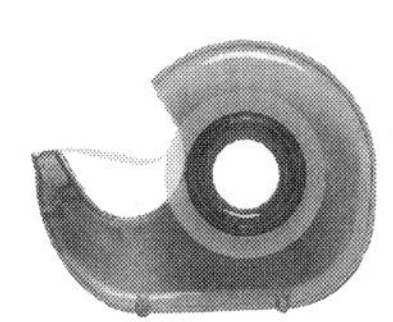
tape

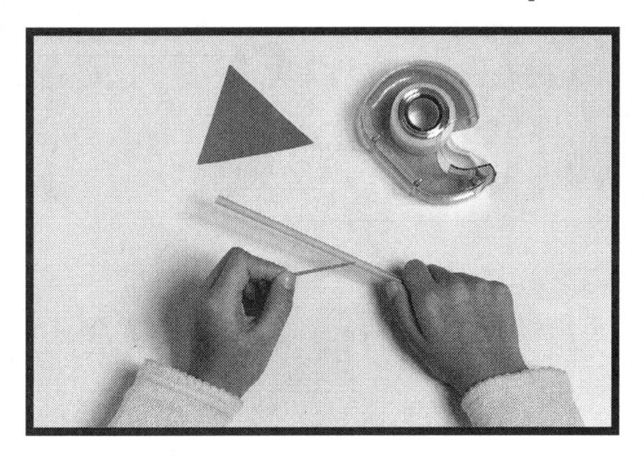

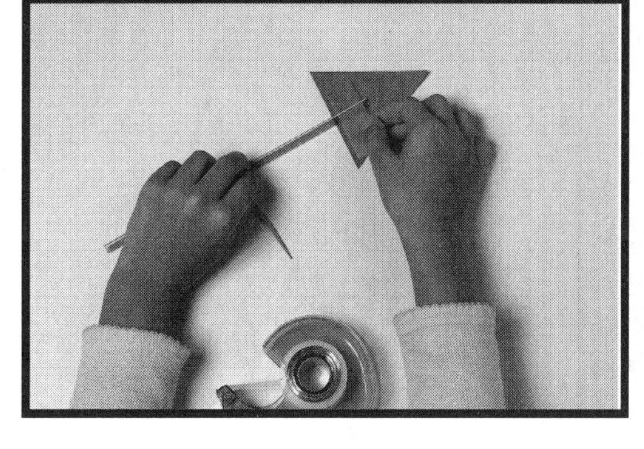

1. Make a wind vane. Poke the toothpick through the straw.

Be careful. Toothpicks are sharp.

2. Tape the paper triangle to the straw.

3. Observe the wind's direction on two windy days.

**Science Skill**
To observe the wind's direction, check which way the triangle points.

Name ______________________ Date ______________

# What Makes Clouds and Rain?

## Investigate

## How Clouds Form

**You will need**

jar with lid

very warm water

ice cubes

1. Pour warm water into the jar. Wait. Pour out most of the water.

Be careful. Water is hot!

2. Set the lid upside down on the jar. Observe the jar.

3. Put ice on the lid. Observe. Infer how clouds form.

**Science Skill**

To infer, first observe. Then think about what happened and draw a conclusion.

D16

Name ______________________ Date ______________

# What Is Spring?

**Investigate**

## What Helps Seeds Sprout

**You will need**

4 bean seeds

2 cups

mist bottle

paper towels

hand lens

1. Put a damp paper towel in each cup. Add two seeds to each. Label the cups *winter* and *spring*.
2. Put the *winter* cup in a cold, dark place. Put the *spring* cup in a warm, dark place.
3. Observe the seeds with the hand lens three days later. What can you infer?

**Science Skill**

To infer, first observe, and then think about what you see.

Name ______________________ Date ______________

# What Is Summer?

## Investigate

## Colors That Can Keep You Cool

**You will need**

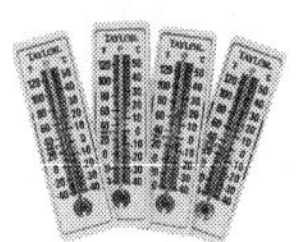

4 thermometers

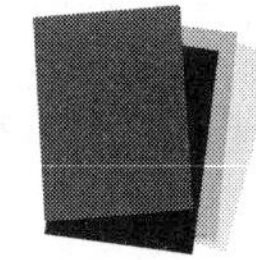

4 colors of paper

stapler

clock

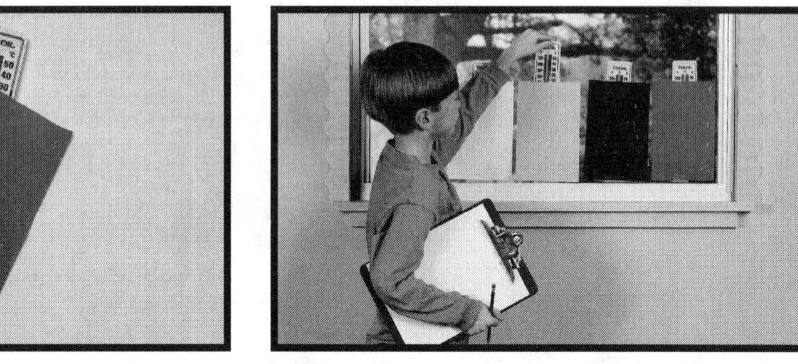

1. Fold and staple 4 color sheets of paper to make sleeves. Put a thermometer in each. Place in the sun.
2. Record the starting temperatures for each.
3. Wait 30 minutes. Record the temperatures again. Order from hottest to coolest.

**Science Skill**

To put the colors in order, start with the one with the hottest temperature. End with the coolest.

D30

Name ________________________ Date ________________

# What Is Fall?

## Investigate

## Storing Apples

**You will need**

apple rings

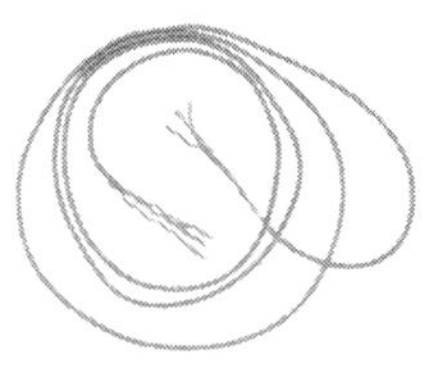
string

plastic bag

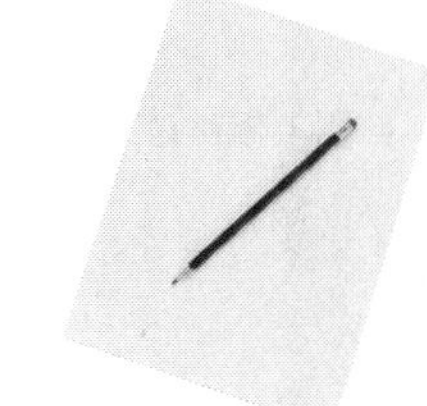
paper and pencil

1. Put some apple rings in the plastic bag. Store them on a shelf.
2. Hang the other apple rings on string. Don't let them touch.
3. Predict and record what will happen.
4. Wait one week. Record.

**Science Skill**

To predict which way to store apple rings is better, use what you know about food. Then decide.

Name ______________________ Date ______________

# What Is Winter?

## Investigate

## Keeping Warm in Cold Weather

**You will need**

plastic bag

container of ice water

things to keep your hand warm

1. Put your hand in the bag. Then put your hand in the ice water. Does the bag keep your hand warm?
2. What could you put in the bag to keep your hand warm? Choose some things to try.
3. Investigate your ideas by trying them. Which one works best?

**Science Skill**

To investigate how to keep your hand warm, try out each of your ideas.

Name ______________________ Date ______________

# What Can We Observe About Solids?

**Investigate**

## Solid Objects

**You will need**

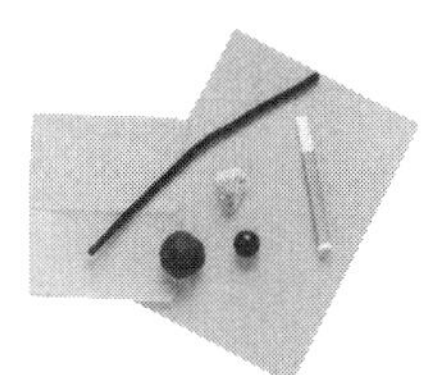

objects

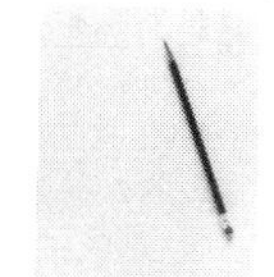

paper and pencil

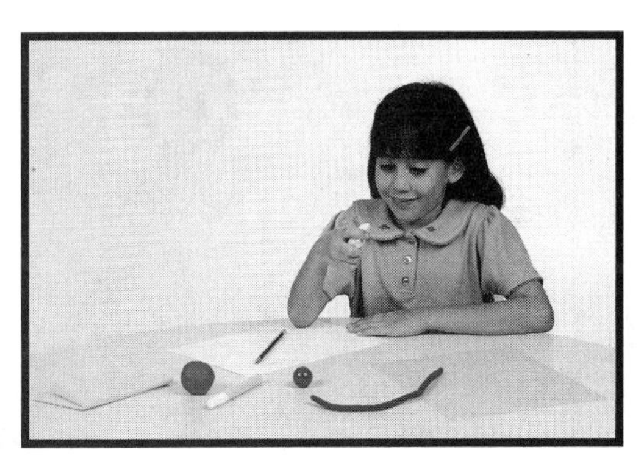

1. Observe each object.
2. Compare the sizes, shapes, and colors of the objects.
3. Think of three ways to classify the objects. Draw or write them on your paper.

**Science Skill**
To classify the objects, find ways they are the same and group them.

Name ______________________ Date ______________

# What Can We Observe About Liquids?

**Investigate**

## Liquids in Bottles

**You will need**

3 containers

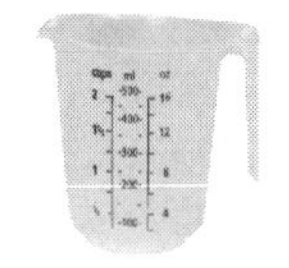

measuring cup

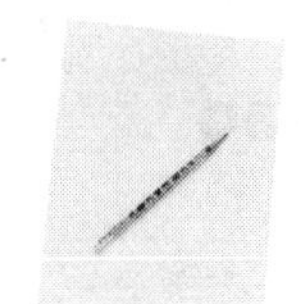

paper and pencil

1. Draw the shape of the water in each container.
2. Which container do you think has the most water?
3. Measure the water. Write a number for each container. Use the numbers to tell what you found out.

**Science Skill**

You can write numbers when you measure. Use the numbers to compare the things you measured.

E8





Use with page E8.

Name ______________________ Date ______________

# What Objects Sink or Float?

**Investigate**

## Shapes That Sink or Float

**You will need**

ball of clay

aquarium with water

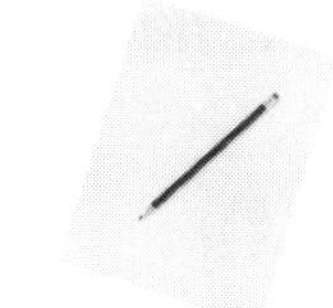

paper and pencil

1. Gather data about shapes that sink or float. Put the clay ball in the water.
2. Record data about what happens.
3. Make the clay into different shapes. Do they sink or float? Record.

**Science Skill**
When you gather data, you observe things. When you record data, you write and draw what you observe.

Name ______________________ Date ______________

# What Can We Observe About Gases?

**Investigate**

## Air in a Bottle

**You will need**

balloon

plastic soft drink bottle

1. Squeeze the bottle to observe the air in it. Blow up the balloon. Feel the air come out.
2. Put the balloon in the bottle. Pull the end over the top.
3. Try to blow up the balloon. What else is in the bottle? Draw a conclusion.

**Science Skill**
To draw a conclusion about what happened, think about what you observed.

E16





Use with page E16.

Name ________________________ Date ________________

# How Can We Change Objects?

Investigate

## Changing Paper

**You will need**

4 cards with slits

paints and brushes

glitter

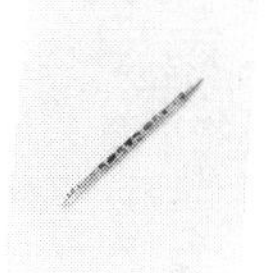

paper and pencil

glue

1. Observe the cards. Record how they look and feel.
2. How could you change the way the cards look and feel? Investigate your ideas.
3. Record how you change the cards.

**Science Skill**
To investigate, think of changes you could make, and then try them out.

E20

Name ______________________ Date ______________

# What Happens When Objects Are Taken Apart?

## Investigate

## Wheels and an Axle

**You will need**

2 paper plates

ballpoint pen

1. Make a model of two wheels and an axle. Poke the pen through the plates. Do the plate wheels roll?

Be careful. The pen point is sharp!

2. Take apart the wheels and axle. Do the wheels roll? Draw a conclusion.

**Science Skill**
When you make a model of something, you can use it to find out how the real thing works.

E24





Use with page E24.

Name ____________________ Date ____________

# What Is Heat?

## Investigate

## What Heat Does to Water

**You will need**

2 cups with water

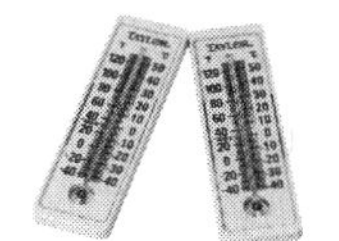

2 thermometers

paper and pencil

clock

1. Measure the temperature of the water in each cup.
2. Make a chart. Write a number to show each temperature.
3. Wait 10 minutes. Read and record each temperature.
4. Draw a conclusion.

**Science Skill**

Use numbers to tell what you found out. Compare the numbers. Draw a conclusion.

Name ______________________ Date ______________

# How Does Heat Change Matter?

## Investigate

## How Heat Changes Water

**You will need**

food coloring

hot water in a bowl

cold water in a bowl

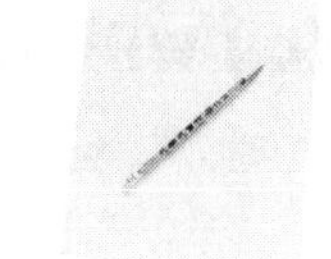

paper and pencil

1. Gather data about how heat changes water. Put a drop of food coloring in cold water. Record.
2. Put a drop of food coloring in hot water. Record.

Be careful. Hot!

3. How did heat change the water? Tell what you found out.

**Science Skill**

To gather data about something, observe it. Then draw or write to record your observations.

E38

Name ______________________ Date ______________

# What Is Light?

## Investigate

## Light and Color

**You will need**

prism

objects

paper and pencil

crayons or markers

flashlight

1. Shine a light. Look at objects through the prism.
2. Draw a picture of what you observe. Label it with the colors you observe.
3. Use your picture to communicate what you observed.

**Science Skill**

To communicate, use the labeled picture to talk about what you observed.

E42

Name ______________________ Date ______________

# What Can Light Do?

## Investigate

## Making Light Bounce

**You will need**

flashlight with battery

index card in clay

mirror

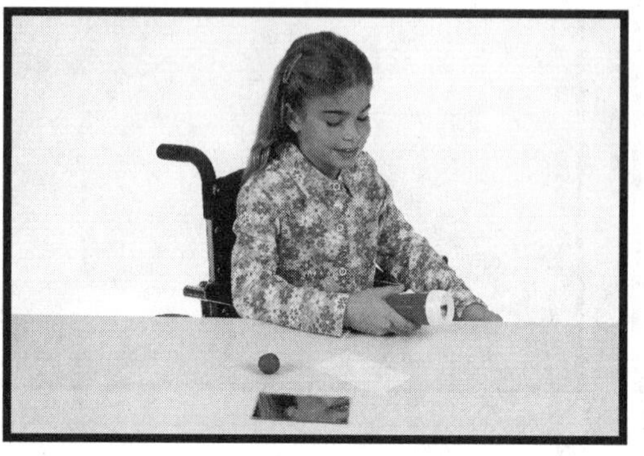

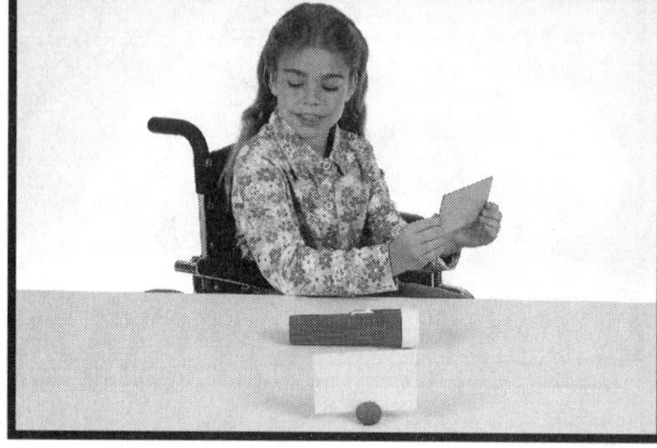

1. Turn the flashlight on. Observe the light.
2. Put the mirror in front of the light. Move the mirror. Observe.
3. Investigate this problem. How can you make light shine on the card without moving the card?

**Science Skill**
To investigate a problem, you plan and try different ideas.

E46



 Use with page E46.

Name ______________________ Date ______________

# What Makes Things Move?

## Investigate

## Pushes and Pulls

**You will need**

small block

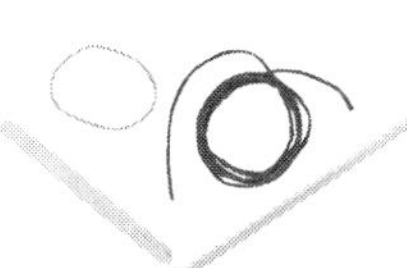
things to make the block move

paper and pencil

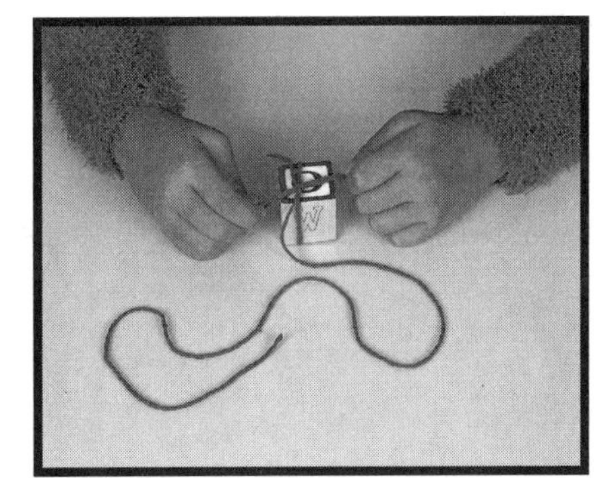

1. What could you do to push or pull the block?
2. Write a plan to investigate your ideas. Then follow your plan.
3. Tell what you used to move the block. Use the word *push* or *pull*.

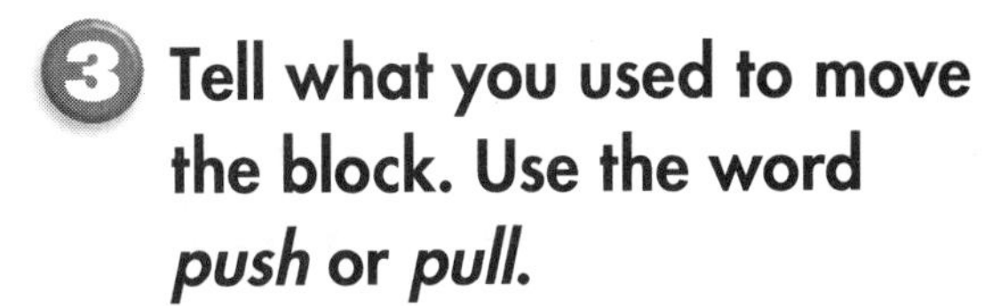

**Science Skill**
You investigate by thinking of ideas and trying them out.

Name ______________________ Date ______________

# What Are Some Ways Things Move?

## Investigate

## Moving Objects

**You will need**

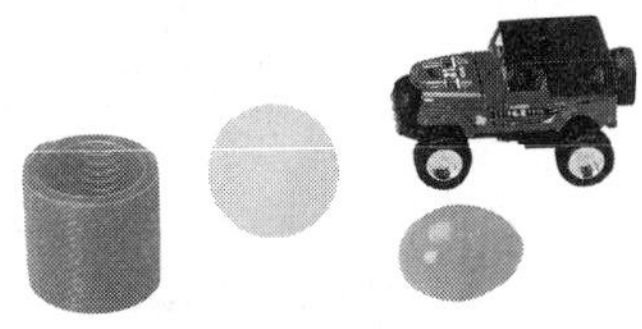

objects

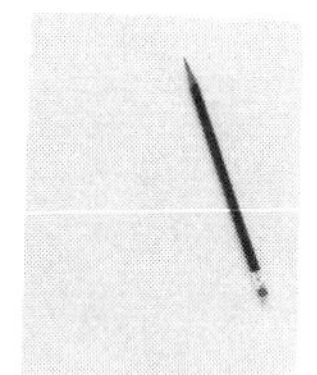

paper and pencil

1. Observe and record how each object moves when you push or pull it.

2. Group objects that move the same way. Write how you grouped them.

**Science Skill**

To group the objects, put those that move in the same way together.

F8





Use with page F8.

Name ____________________ Date ____________

# Why Do Things Move the Way They Do?

## Investigate

## Predicting Motion

**You will need**

ramp

plastic ball

tape

block

1. Set up the ramp. Predict where the ball will stop. Mark that place with tape.
2. Let the ball roll down the ramp. Was your prediction right?
3. Now put the block where the ball will hit it. Do Steps 1 and 2 again.

**Science Skill**
To predict where the ball will stop, think about how a ball rolls and bounces.

F12

Name ______________________ Date ______________

# How Do Objects Move on Surfaces?

## Investigate

## Smooth and Rough Surfaces

**You will need**

ramp

toy truck

meterstick

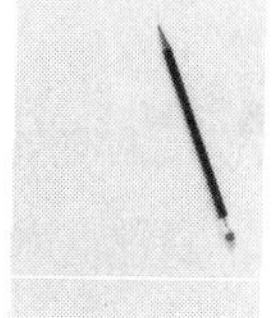

paper and pencil

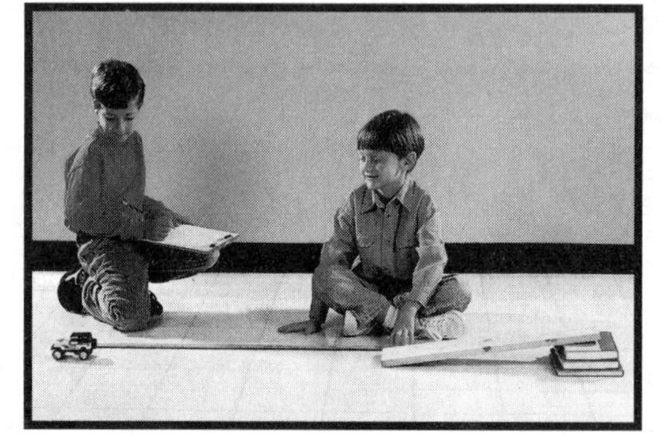

1. Set up a ramp on a smooth surface. Let the car roll down.
2. Measure how far it rolls. Record the number. Do the same on a rough surface.
3. On which surface does the car roll farther? Use your numbers to tell.

**Science Skill**

Measure how far the car rolls from the end of the ramp to where the car stops.

F18





Use with page F18.

Name ______________________ Date ______________

# How Do Wheels Help Objects Move?

## Investigate

### Rollers

**You will need**

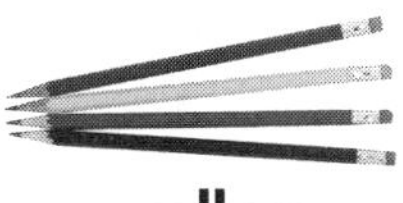
rollers

heavy book

toy truck

tape

1. Push the book. Then put rollers under it. Push again. Which is easier?
2. Push the truck. Tape the wheels, and push it again. Which is easier?
3. Draw a conclusion about wheels and rollers.

**Science Skill**
To draw a conclusion about something, use what you have observed to explain what happens.

F22

Name ______________________ Date ______________

# What Are Magnets?

**Investigate**

## What a Magnet Can Do

**You will need**

bar magnet

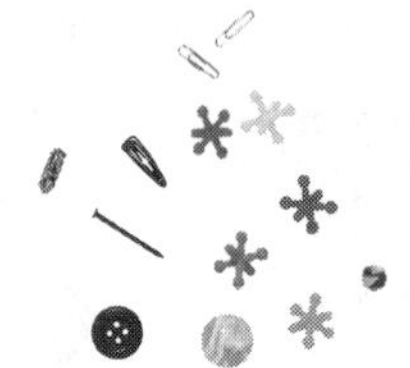

objects

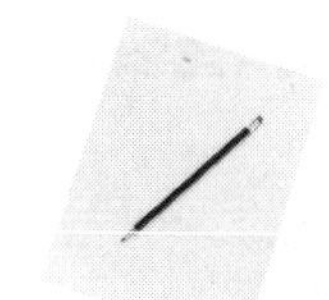

paper and pencil

| What a Magnet Can Do | | |
|---|---|---|
| Object | Pulls | Does Not Pull |
| | | |

1. Gather data about the magnet. Hold it near each object.
2. Make a chart like this one. Record what you observe.
3. Group the objects the magnet pulls and those it does not pull.

**Science Skill**
To gather data about what a magnet can do, observe and record what it does.

F32





Use with page F32.

Name ____________________ Date ____________________

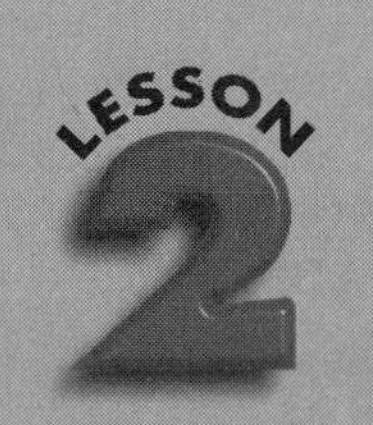


# What Are the Poles of a Magnet?

**Investigate**

## A Magnet's Ends

**You will need**

bar magnet

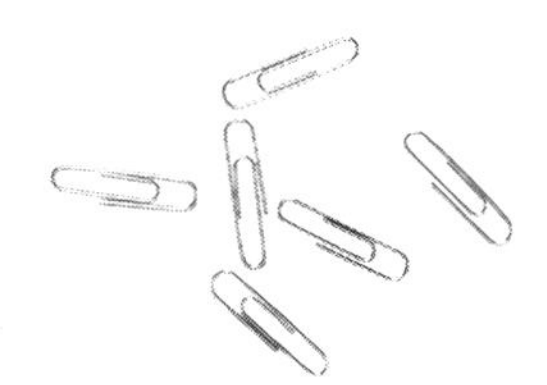

paper clips

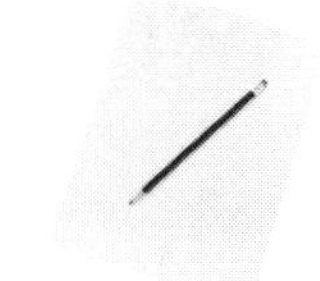

paper and pencil

1. Pick up paper clips with one end of the magnet. Record the number. Then do the other end.
2. Pick up paper clips with the middle of the magnet. Record the number.
3. Make a bar graph. Infer which parts of the magnet are strongest.

**Science Skill**

To infer which parts of the magnet are the strongest, compare the numbers in your bar graph.

Name ______________________ Date ______________

# What Can a Magnet Pull Through?

## Investigate

## Things Magnets Pull Through

**You will need**

bar magnet

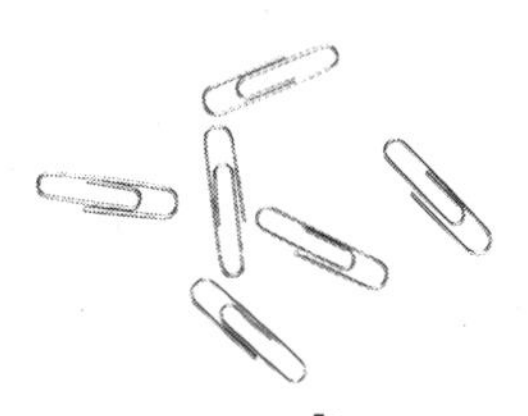

paper clips

different materials

1. Can a magnet attract paper clips through things? Plan an investigation to find out. Write your plan.

2. Follow your plan to investigate your ideas. Record what you observe.

3. Use your data to communicate what you find out.

**Science Skill**

To investigate what things a magnet can pull through, first make a plan and then try your ideas.

F42





Use with page F42.

Name ____________________ Date ____________

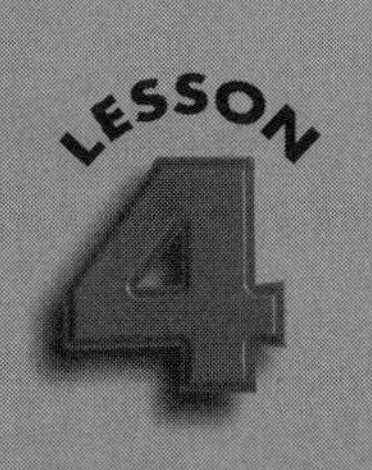


# How Can You Make a Magnet?

## Investigate

## Making a Magnet

**You will need**

magnet

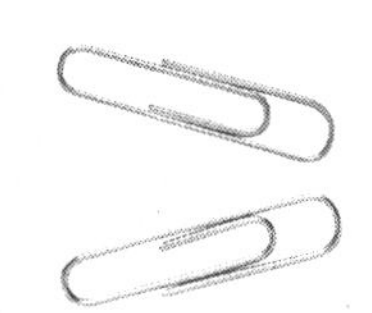
2 paper clips

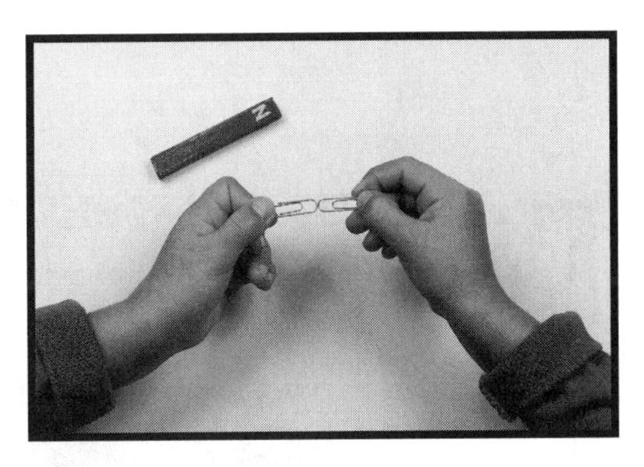

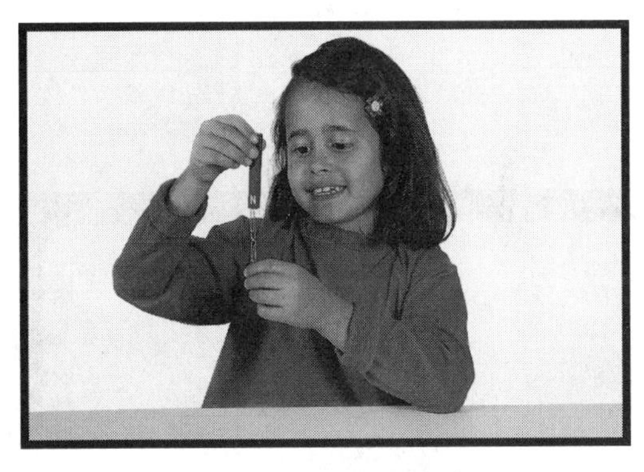

1. Touch one clip to the other. Observe.
2. Use the magnet to pick up one clip. Touch that clip to the other one. Observe.
3. Take away the magnet. Draw a conclusion. How can you make a magnet?

**Science Skill**

To draw a conclusion, use what you have observed to form an idea.

F46

# Picture Cards

**Card #1**
**spruce tree**

**Card #2**
**spruce cone**

**Card #3**
**watermelon slice**

**Card #4**
**strawberries**

# Picture Cards

**Card #5**
**peanuts**

**Card #6**
**swan**

**Card #7**
**cygnets**

**Card #8**
**alligator**

# Picture Cards

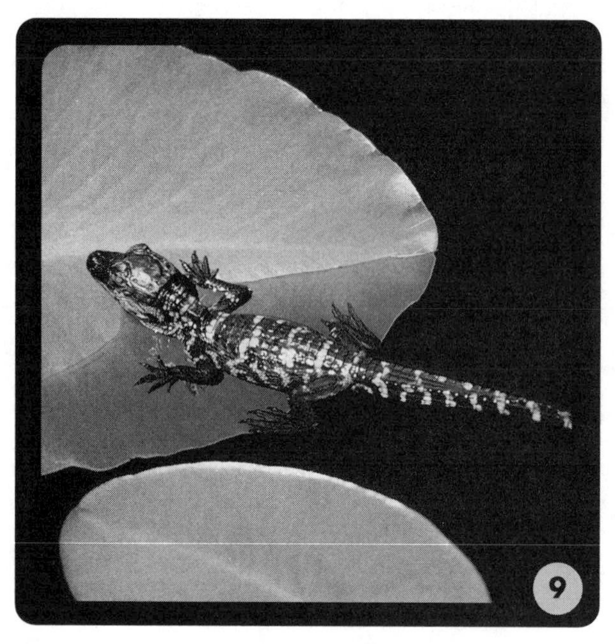

**Card #9**
**young alligator**

**Card #10**
**elephant**

**Card #11**
**elephant calf**

**Card #12**
**cat**

# Picture Cards

**Card #13**
**kitten**

**Card #14**
**sea turtle**

**Card #15**
**young sea turtle**

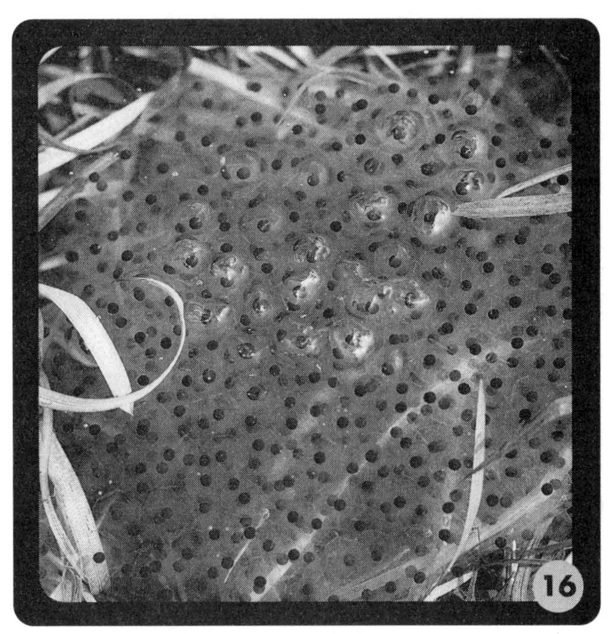


**Card #16**
**frog eggs**

# Picture Cards

**Card #17**
**tadpole**

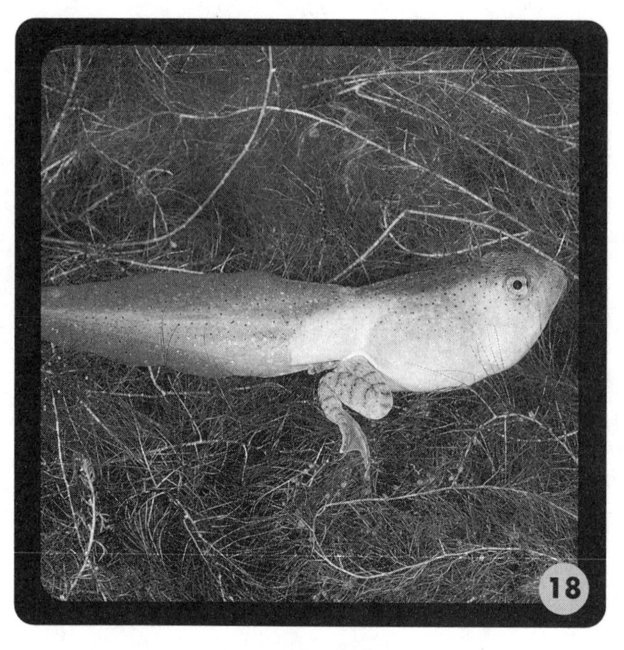

**Card #18**
**tadpole with back legs**

**Card #19**
**tadpole with front legs**

**Card #20**
**frog**

# Picture Cards

**Card #21**
**baseball bat**

**Card #22**
**straw basket**

**Card #23**
**newspapers**

**Card #24**
**cotton T-shirt**

# Picture Cards

**Card #25**
**wooden dresser**

**Card #26**
**leather boots**

**Card #27**
**wool sweater**

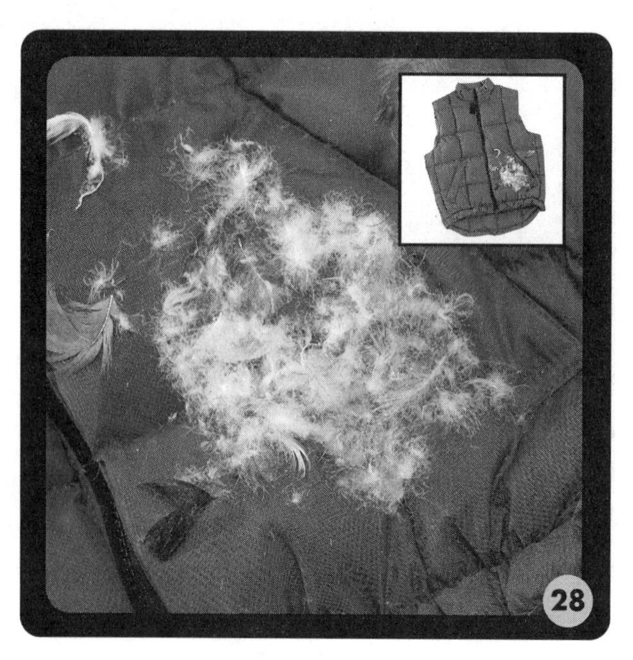

**Card #28**
**goose down vest**

# Picture Cards

**Card #29**
**leather baseball mitt and ball**

**Card #30**
**leather briefcase**

**Card #31**
**parrotfish**

**Card #32**
**dolphin**

# Picture Cards

**Card #33**
**shark**

**Card #34**
**barracuda**

**Card #35**
**turtle**

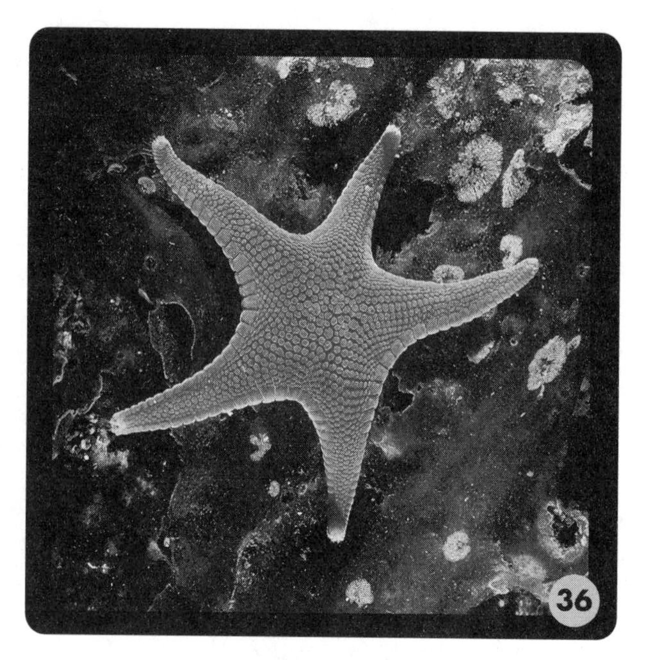


**Card #36**
**starfish**

# Picture Cards

**Card #37**
**anemone**

**Card #38**
**coral**

**Card #39**
**grouper**

**Card #40**
**sponge**

# Writing in Science

## Model: Information Sentences

You can write **information sentences** that tell about something. Answer the questions *Who? What? Where?* and *When?*

A bird is an animal that has feathers and wings. Mother birds lay eggs. Some birds live on land. Some live near water. Many birds fly south for the winter.

# Writing in Science

## Model: Description

When you write a **description,** you tell about something you observe. You use words that tell how the thing looks, sounds, tastes, smells, or feels.

Our class visited the seashore last week. The waves were noisy, and the air smelled fishy. We saw big brown seagulls. I brought back some soft white sand.

Name ______________________ Date ______________

# Animals and Their Young

| Animal | Same | Different |
|---|---|---|
| cats | Both have ears.<br>Both are orange. | One is big.<br>One is small. |
| | | |
| | | |
| | | |
| | | |
| | | |
| | | |





Use with page A58.

Name ______________________ Date ______________

# Rocks

| Red | | | |
|---|---|---|---|
| | | | |

Name ______________________ Date ______________

# Soil

| Looks | Smells | Feels |
| --- | --- | --- |
| | | |





Use with page C8.

Name ____________________ Date ____________

## Inside

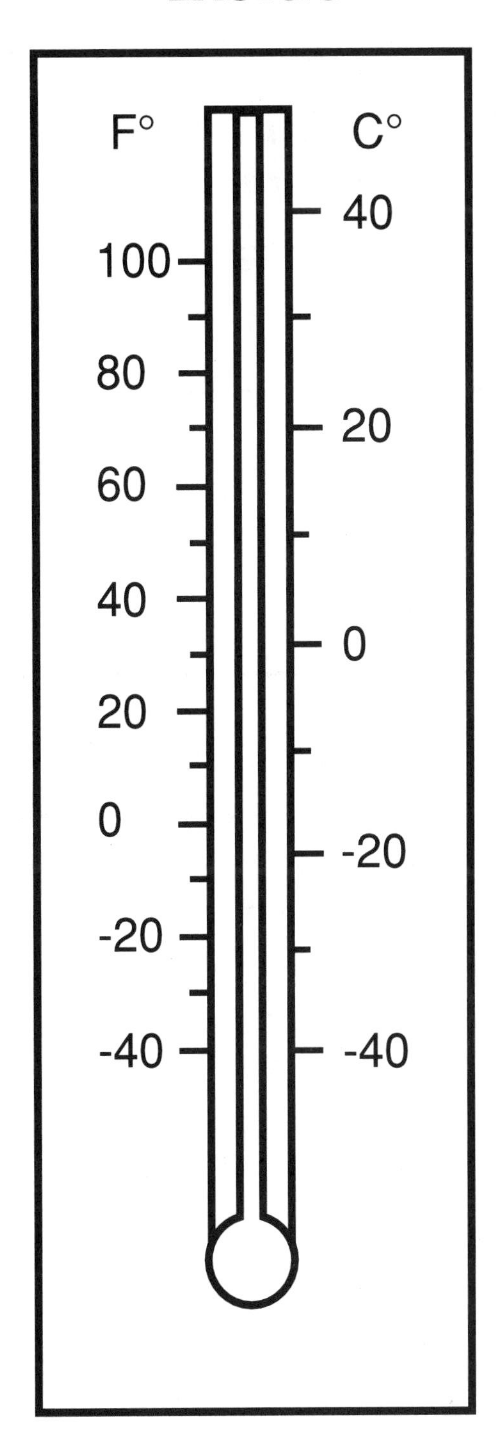


## Outside

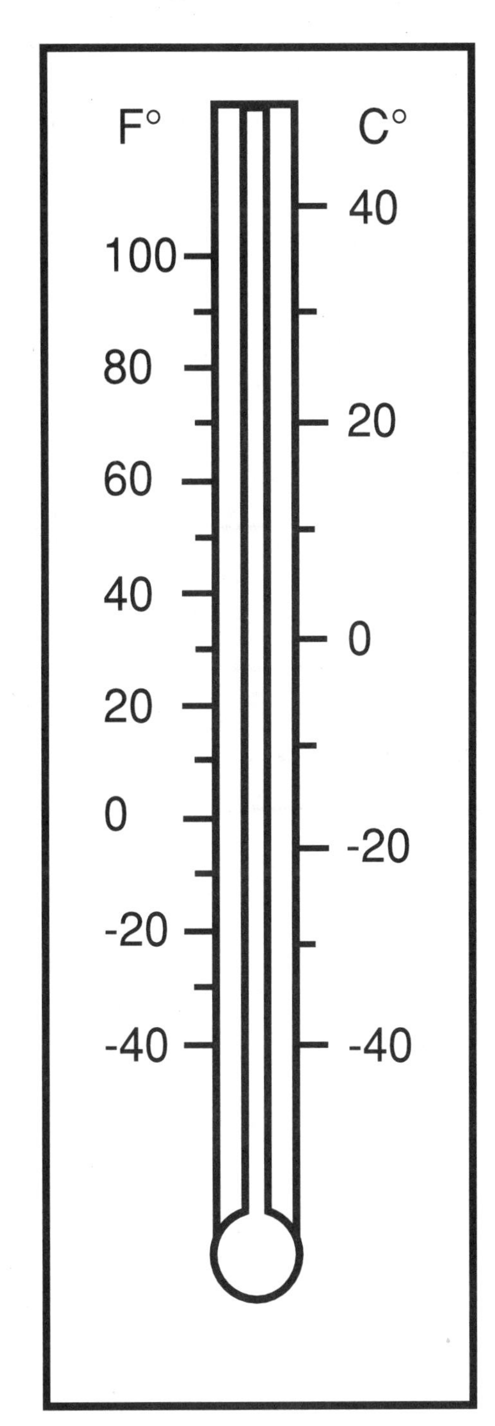

Name ______________________ Date ______________

# Temperature

| Color | Start | 30 minutes later |
|---|---|---|
| white | | |
| black | | |
| red | | |
| yellow | | |





Use with page D30.

Name ______________________ Date ______________

# Water Temperature

| Cup of water | Start | After 10 minutes |
| --- | --- | --- |
| in shade | | |
| in sunlight | | |

Name ______________________ Date ______________

# What a Magnet Can Do

| Object | Pulls | Does not pull |
|---|---|---|
| | | |
| | | |
| | | |
| | | |
| | | |
| | | |
| | | |
| | | |
| | | |
| | | |





Use with page F32.

Name ______________________ Date ______________

UNIT A
# Activities
for Home or School

## Senses Game

Get a box and put in different things. Ask your family or classmates to close their eyes. Have them use touch and hearing to guess each thing.

## Nature Walk

Take a nature walk with your class or with family members. Draw or write about what you observe.

Name ______________________ Date ______________

## Growing and Changing

Look at photos of yourself with a family member. Talk about how you have changed.

## Observe a Pet

With an adult, find a pet to observe. Draw or write about the animal.

What does the pet look like?

What does it eat and drink?

A79

Name ______________________ Date ______________

UNIT B

# Activities

for Home or School

## What Do Worms Need?

Find out which soil worms like best.

1. Put two kinds of soil and two worms in a covered box.
2. In two hours, check where the worms are.
3. What do the worms need? Talk about what you observe.

## Make a Bird Feeder

1. Spread peanut butter on a pinecone.
2. Roll the pinecone in birdseed.
3. Hang the pinecone with string outdoors.
4. Observe birds that eat the seeds.

B46





Use with page B46.

Name ______________________ Date ______________

## Rain Forest in a Jar

1. Put pebbles, soil, and plants in a jar.
2. Water the plants. Put the lid on the jar.
3. Put the jar where it gets light but not strong sun.
4. Wait one day. Observe. How is this like a rainforest?

## Stems That Store Water

1. Observe the stem pipes, or small dots on a cut celery stalk.
2. Set the stalk in an empty cup. Put it in the sun until it droops.
3. Add water to the cup. Put it in the refrigerator. The next day, tell what happened and why.



B47

Name ______________________ Date ______________

UNIT C
# Activities
for Home or School

## Observe Soil Layers

1. Put soil in a jar.
2. Fill the jar with water.
3. Put the lid on tight.
4. Wait for the soil to settle. Draw what you observe.

## Make a Soil Key

1. Fold an index card into four parts. Cut a hole in the middle.
2. Color each part black, brown, yellow-orange, or orange-brown.
3. Put the card on top of some soil near your home. Which color matches?
4. Brown and black soils are good for growing plants. Tell about your soil.

Name ______________________ Date ______________

## How Much Air Is In a Breath?

1. Take a big breath.
2. Let it out by blowing into a balloon.
3. With your fingers, hold the end of the balloon closed. Observe how much air you breathed out.
4. Compare balloon breaths to a classmate's or family member's.

## Visit a Shoreline

1. With your class or family members, visit a shoreline.
2. Observe the soil. Dig at it.
3. Draw pictures of any shells, rocks, plants, or animals you observe.
4. Share your drawings.

Name ____________________ Date ____________

UNIT D

# Activities

for Home or School

## Make a Sail for a Car

Put a paper sail on a toy car. Blow on the sail to make the car move. What could you do to make a better sail? Try your ideas.

## Investigate Water Vapor

1. With an adult present, blow into a small plastic bag.
2. Observe the water drops inside. They come from the water vapor in your breath.
3. Put the bag in a freezer for five minutes. Tell what happens.
4. Put the bag in the sun for five minutes. Tell what happens.

Name ______________________ Date ______________

## Make a Four Seasons Poster

Fold a big sheet of paper into four parts. Label each part for a different season. Add pictures of things you like to do in each season. Talk about your poster.

## Find Seasons in a Closet

What clothes do people wear at different times of the year where you live? Brainstorm ideas. Write a list that shows at least two things for each season.

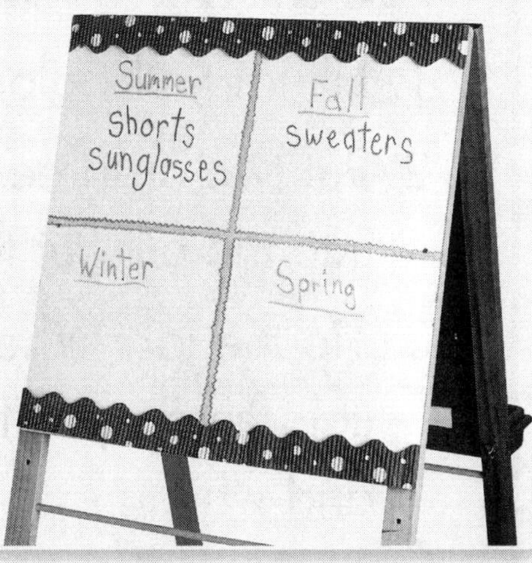


**D47**

Name ____________________ Date ____________

UNIT E
# Activities
for Home or School

## Make Juice Bars

Change liquid juice into a solid by making juice pops.

1. Have a family member help you pour fruit juice into an ice cube tray.
2. Put a toothpick into each part of the tray. *Be careful. Toothpicks are sharp.*
3. Freeze and eat!

## Floating Drops

1. Fill jar with salad oil.
2. Put two or three drops of food coloring into the oil. Put the lid on the jar.
3. Tip the jar. What happens to the colored drops? Talk about what floats and why.

Name ______________________ Date ______________

## Be a Shadow Tracker

1. In the morning, put a sheet of paper by a sunny window.
2. Put a stick in a ball of clay on the paper. Trace the stick's shadow. Write the time.
3. Trace the shadow and write the time again two more times that day.
4. Tell what happens to the shadow.

## What Keeps Cold In?

1. Put one ice cube in a foam cup. Put another foam cup on top of that cup.
2. Do the same thing using two clear plastic cups.
3. Put both sets of cups in a warm place.
4. Observe the ice cubes in one hour. Which cups would you use to keep a drink cold?

**E55**

Name ______________________ Date ______________

UNIT F

# Activities

for Home or School

## Magnetic Kite

1. Cut out a tissue paper kite.
2. Attach thread and a paper clip.
3. Tape the thread's tail to a table.
4. Use the magnet to pick up your kite without touching it.

## Magnetic Race-Car Game

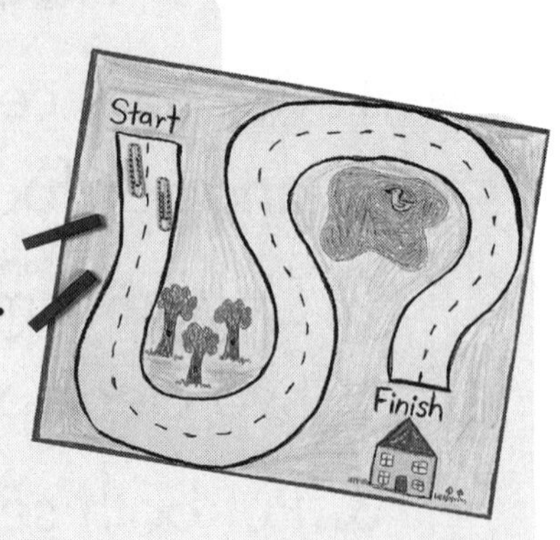


1. Draw roads on cardboard.
2. Put two paper clips on the road.
3. Put two magnets under the cardboard. Move the magnets to race your clips.

Name ______________________ Date ______________

## Make a Water Wheel

1. Push toothpicks into the ends of a piece of clay. *Be careful. Toothpicks are sharp.*
2. Push the end of the carton strips into the clay to make a water wheel.
3. Hold the wheel by the toothpicks. Place the wheel under running water.
4. Tell how the water makes the wheel turn.

## Marble Fun Slide

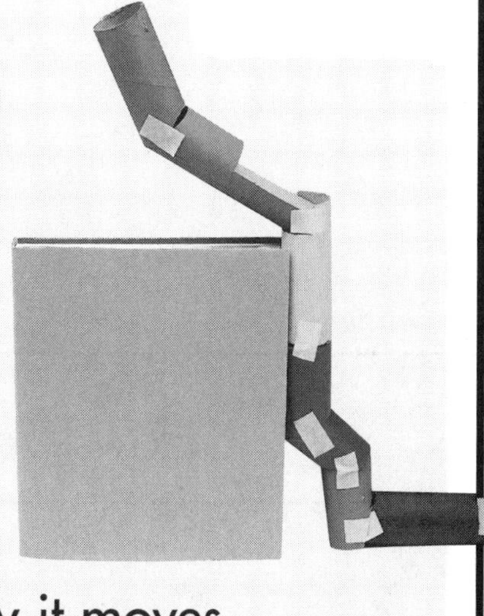

1. Tape together paper towel tubes to make a fun slide.
2. Use books to hold up the tubes.
3. Put a marble at the top, and listen to it race to the bottom. Talk about how it moves.

F55

# Project Plan

## What We Want to Find Out

1.

## How We Can Find Out

2.

## What We Need to Do

| 3. | <u>Materials</u> |
|---|---|
| | |

## How We Can Share Information

4.

# Questions We Have

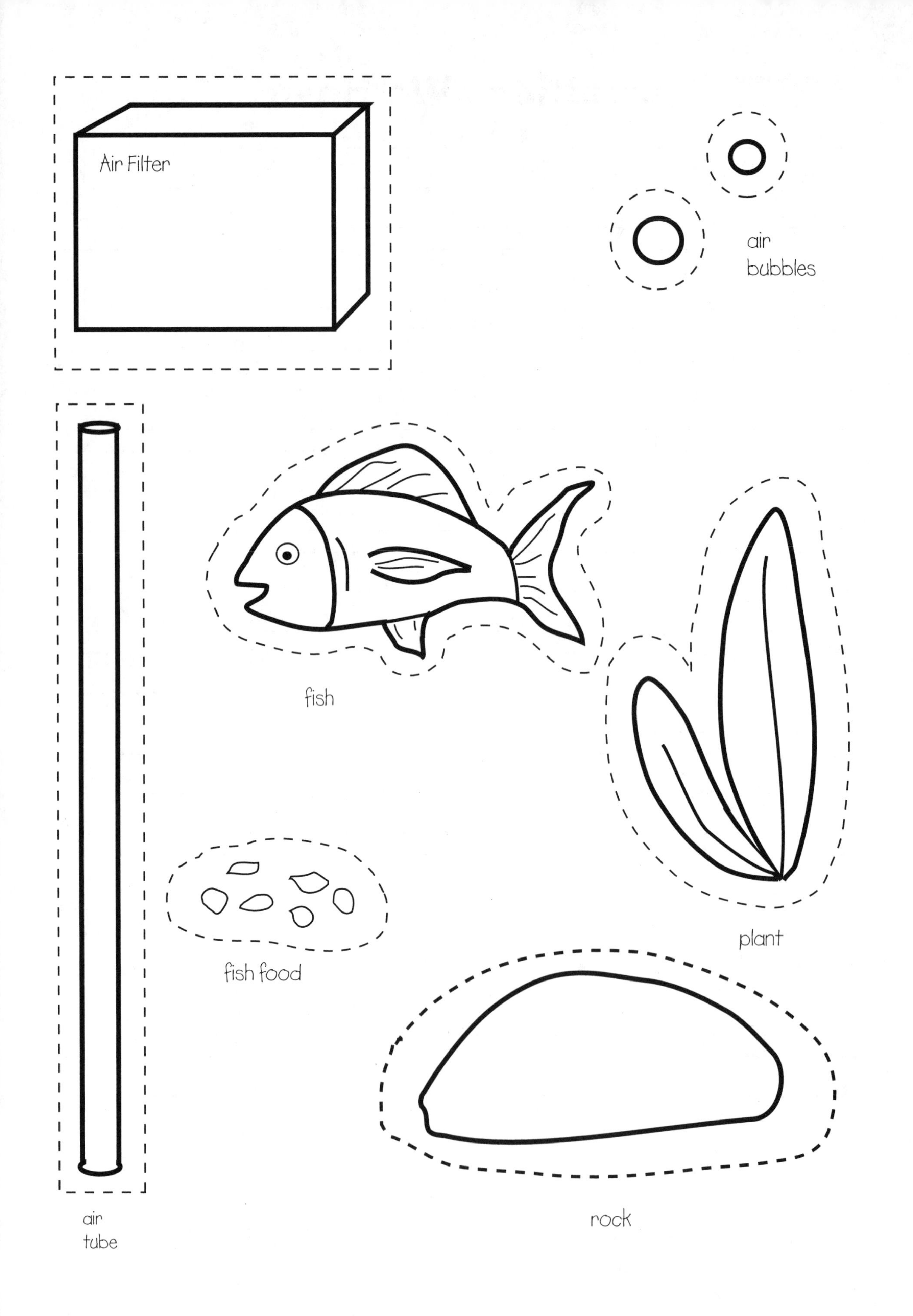
Air Filter
air
bubbles
fish
plant
fish food
rock
air
tube

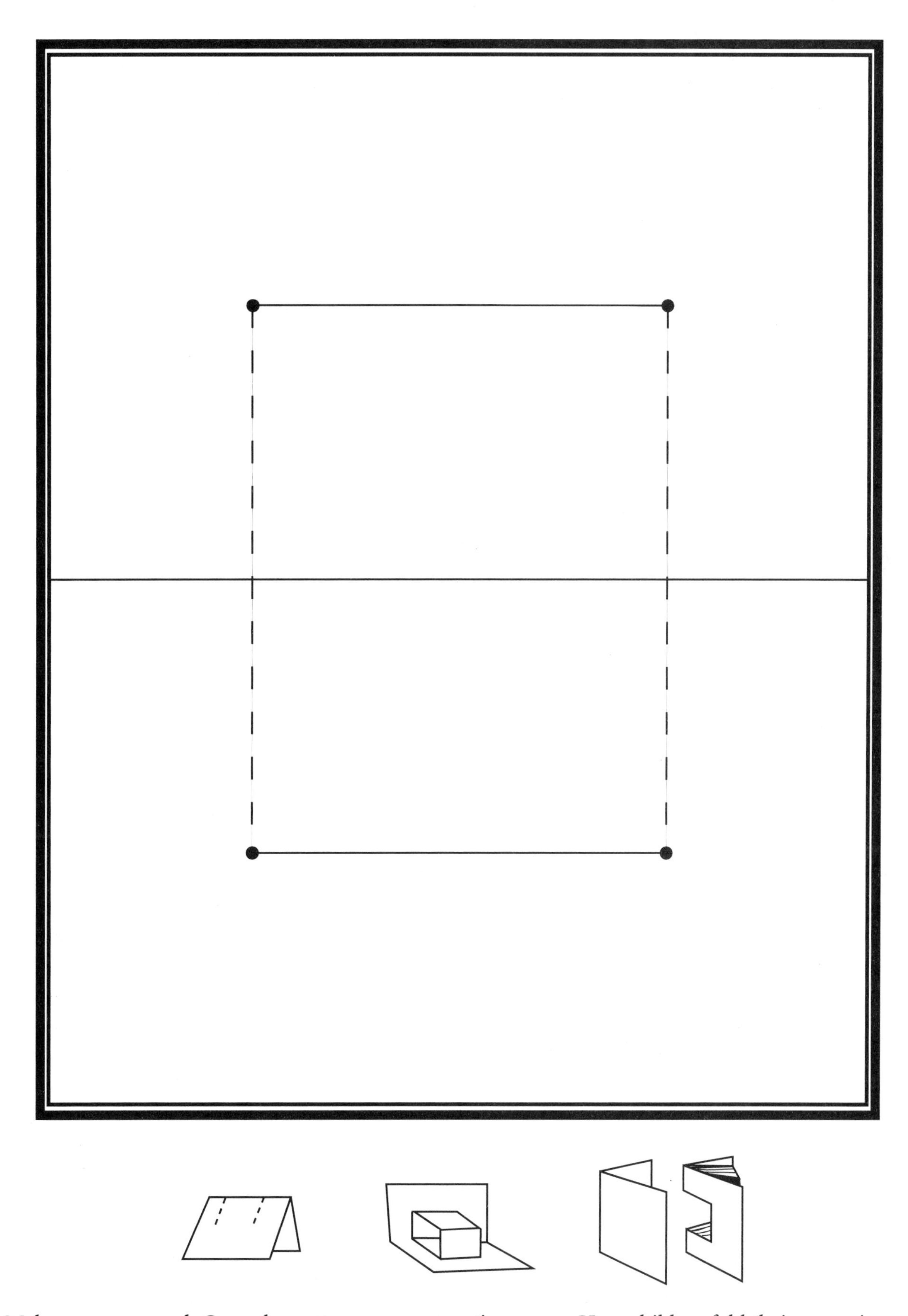

Make a pop-up card. Copy the pattern on construction paper. Have children fold their paper in half and cut along the dotted lines. Help children push the cut area through the fold. Then crease along the solid lines to form the pop-box. Children can glue on an extra sheet.

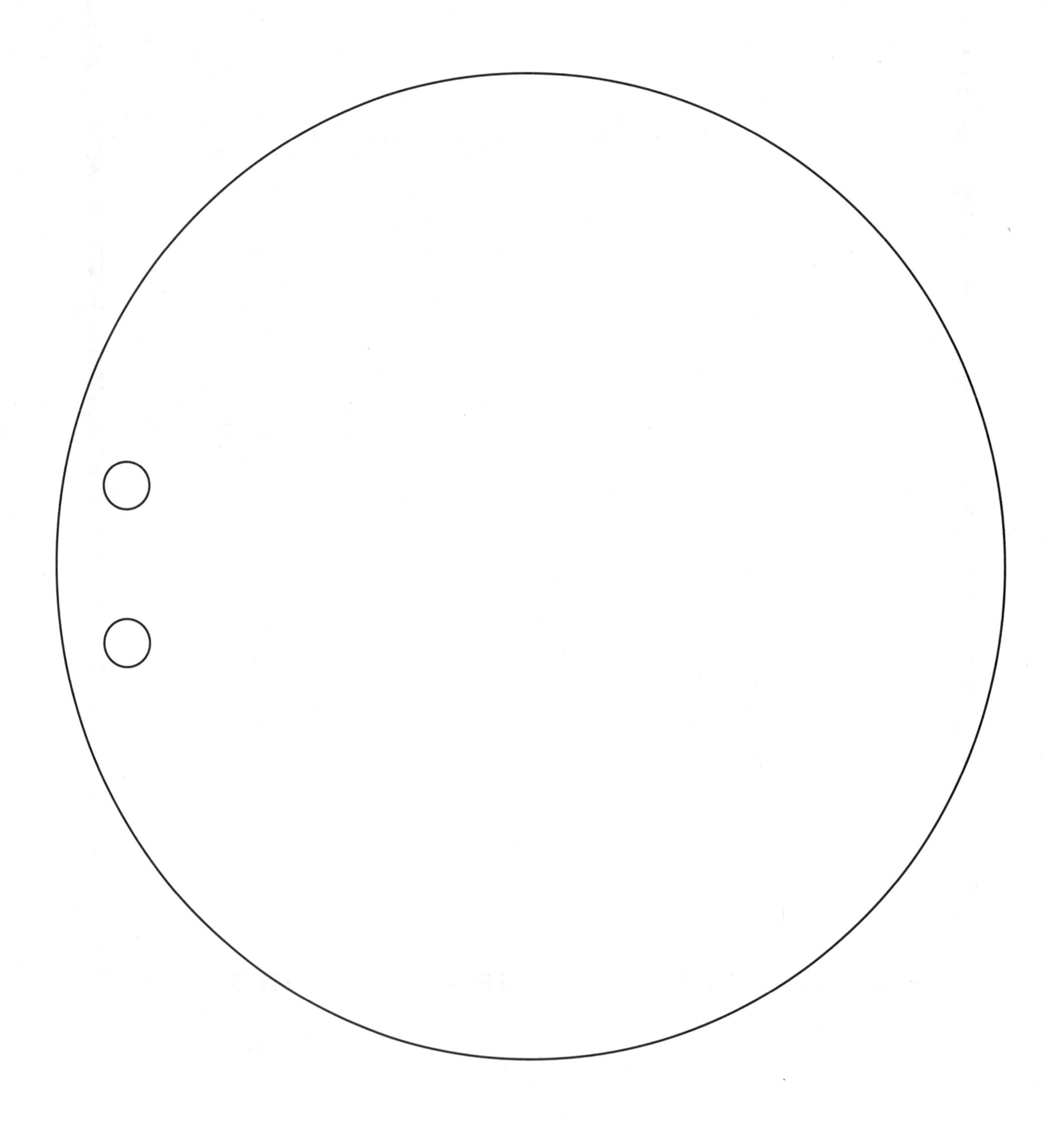





**Use with page C40.**

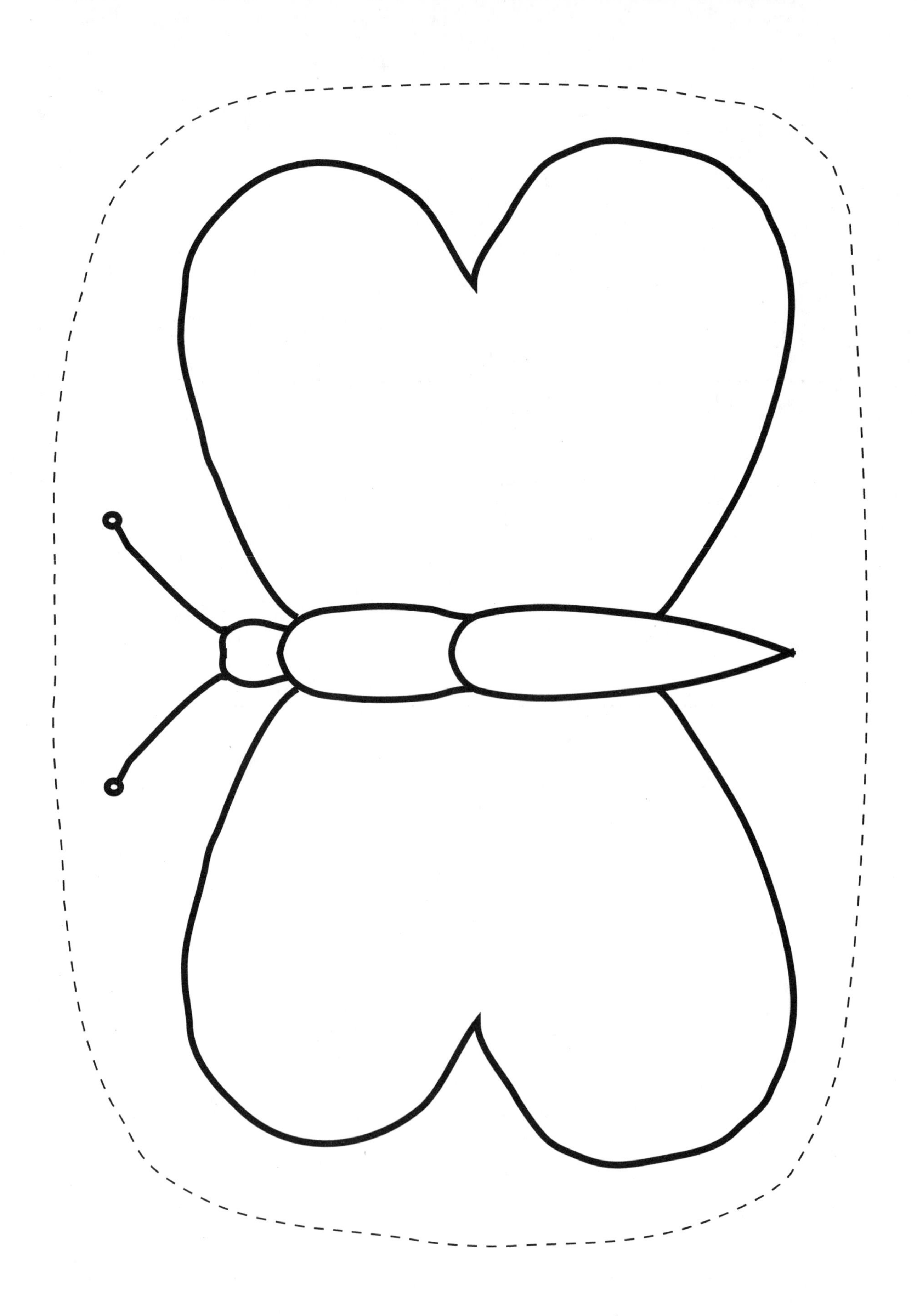

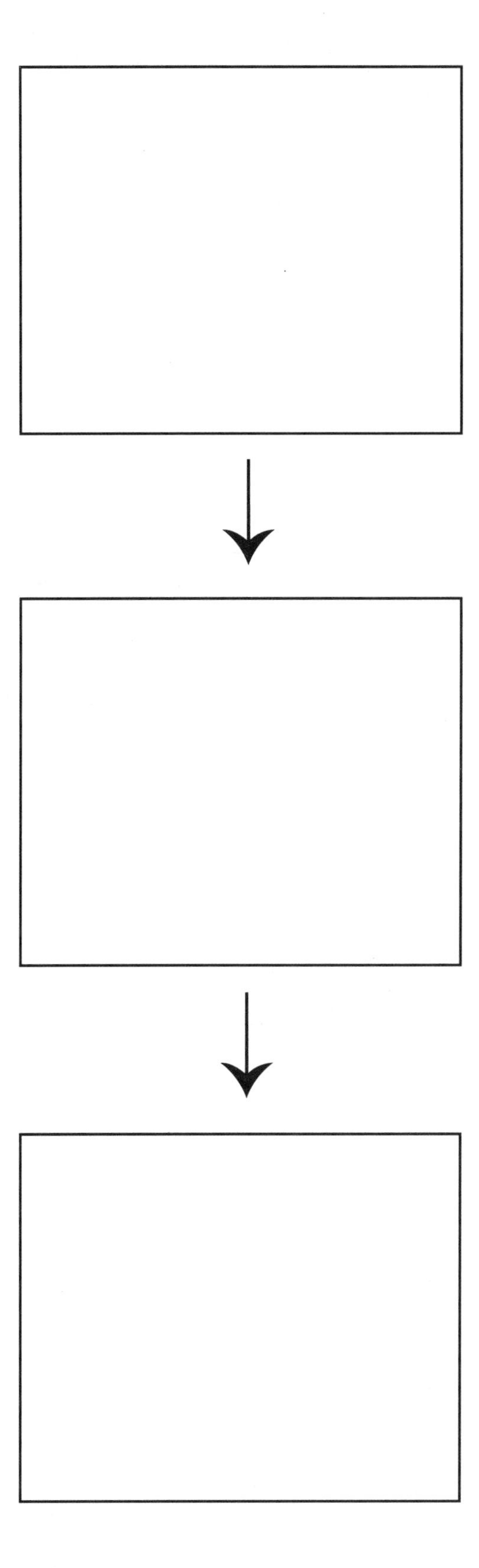

Flowchart

# Venn Diagram

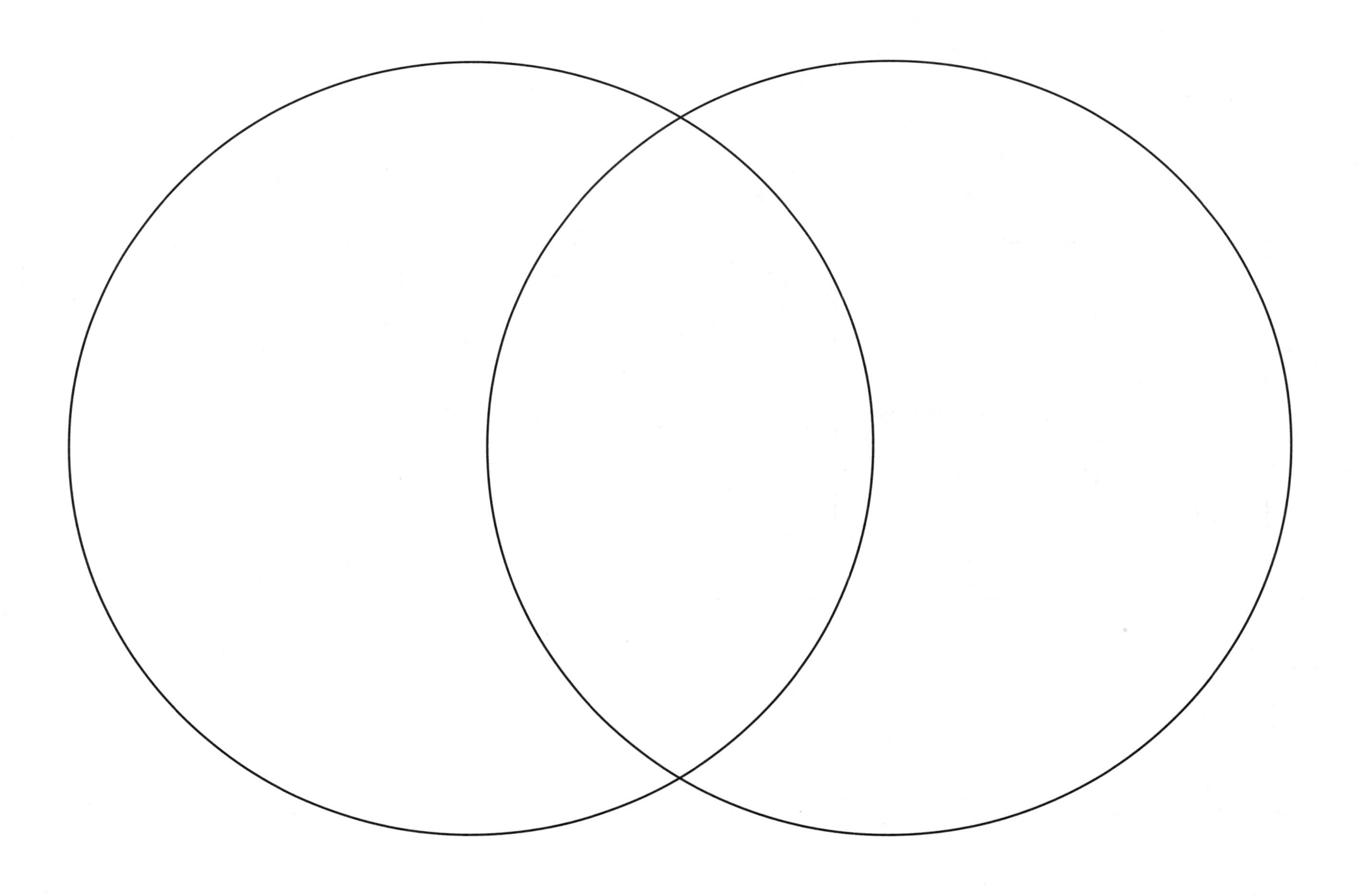

# Computer Notes

# K-W-L Chart

| What I Know | What I Want to Know | What I Learned |
| --- | --- | --- |
| | | |

# Web

# Chart

| | |
|---|---|
| | |